Plan 6921 Milano see page 66

fiorentino

The graceful curves of rotundas, dramatically changing roof pitches and architectural enhancements like half-columns, corbels and an arbor delight the eye with their gentle movement. Guests know they've arrived as they step up to the entry terrace and are embraced by the home's elegant entry.

The gentle curve of the elegant staircase that sweeps upward in a rotunda, the curved windows in the living room and breakfast nook, and the graceful arc of a wet bar and wine room heighten the visual appeal of this plan.

Large windows look longingly onto a loggia, where sunlight and shadow play hide-and-seek between columns. The home hugs this outdoor space, offering different perspectives and experiences from each room. Architectural lighting at night creates an alluring ambience that beckons to be indulged, to be experienced.

The master suite sets the stage for serene interlude, beginning with the elevated garden tub that looks through three arched windows onto a privacy garden and culminating in the bedroom's sitting area overlooking the loggia — meant to be enjoyed with a refreshing beverage from the suite's morning kitchen.

A media room is the ultimate retreat for the owners of the home and the guests enjoying the privacy of two second-floor guest suites. Seclusion is found in the loft overlooking the dining room and the deck above the loggia — an ideal vantage point for stargazing.

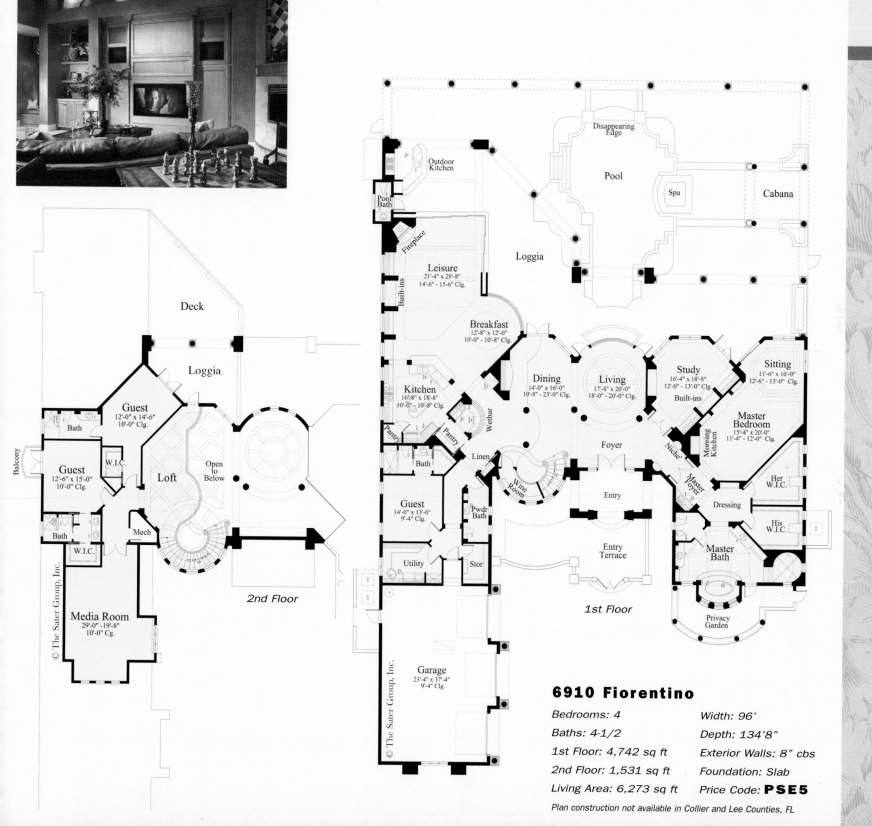

LiteTouch

Deck

Loggia

Guest
12'-0" x 14'-6"
10'-0" Clg.

Bath

Guest
12'-6" x 15'-0"
10'-0" Clg.

W.I.C.

Balcony

Loft

Open to Below

Bath

W.I.C.

Mech

Media Room
29'-0" -19'-8"
10'-0" Cg.

© The Sater Group, Inc.

2nd Floor

Disappearing Edge

Outdoor Kitchen

Pool

Spa

Cabana

Pool Bath

Loggia

Fireplace

Built-ins

Leisure
21'-4" x 28'-8"
14'-6" - 15'-6" Clg.

Breakfast
12'-8" x 12'-0"
10'-0" - 10'-8" Clg.

Dining
14'-0" x 16'-0"
10'-8" - 23'-0" Clg.

Living
17'-8" x 20'-0"
18'-0" - 20'-0" Clg.

Study
16'-4" x 18'-8"
12'-0" - 13'-0" Clg.

Built-ins

Sitting
11'-6" x 10'-0"
12'-6" - 13'-0" Clg.

Master Bedroom
15'-4" x 20'-0"
11'-4" - 12'-0" Clg.

Kitchen
16'-8" x 18'-8"
10'-0" - 10'-8" Clg.

Wetbar

Morning Kitchen

Niche'

Her W.I.C.

Pantry

Pantry

Bath

Linen

Foyer

Master Foyer

Dressing

His W.I.C.

Wine Room

Guest
14'-0" x 13'-0"
9'-4" Clg.

Pwdr Bath

Entry

Entry Terrace

Master Bath

Utility

Stor

Privacy Garden

© The Sater Group, Inc.

1st Floor

Garage
23'-4" x 37'-4"
9'-4" Clg.

6910 Fiorentino

Bedrooms: 4

Baths: 4-1/2

1st Floor: 4,742 sq ft

2nd Floor: 1,531 sq ft

Living Area: 6,273 sq ft

Width: 96'

Depth: 134'8"

Exterior Walls: 8" cbs

Foundation: Slab

Price Code: PSE5

Plan construction not available in Collier and Lee Counties, FL

5

sterling oaks

Timeless columns, multiple sunburst-arched openings, a grand porte cochere, and an illuminating stairwell are deserving of an ovation. As you walk through this home's 5,816 square feet of living area, a drama awaits at every turn.
The living room's curved coffered ceiling accents the 22-foot, true-arch bowed glass wall that borders the unfolding rear verandahs.

Encased in corner-pocket sliding doors, the leisure room sets the stage for evening entertainment. A glass-enclosed adjoining nook complements the shapely full-featured kitchen. A stepped ceiling gallery leads to the secluded master suite, with its own access to the verandah and private garden off the master bath. Multiple verandahs and private decks supply vivid, outdoor images to complete this home's magical presence.

Wrought-iron rimmed balconies overlook the tropical patio and pool area. The extensive verandah offers comfortable outdoor living, complete with its own kitchen and bar.

If your idea of entertainment is cooking for an audience, this octagonal kitchen puts you center stage. Custom cabinetry and a central island supply everything you need within easy reach.

Extensive use of exterior glass expands the feeling of interior spaces. The verandah just beyond the living room immediately greets you upon entry, and magnificent views follow at every turn.

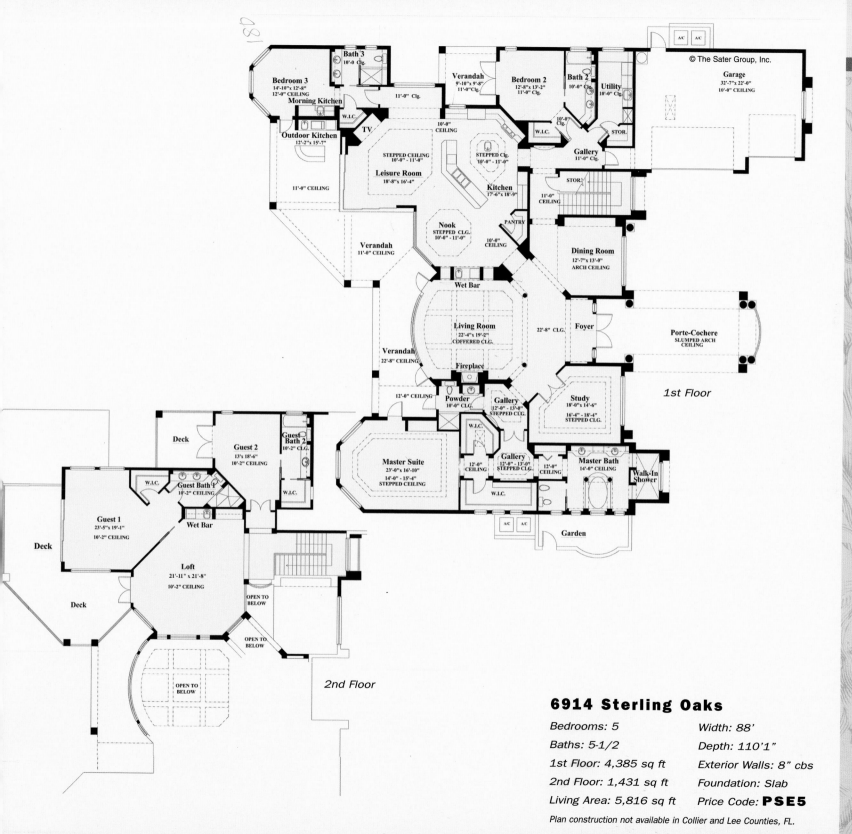

© The Sater Group, Inc.

1st Floor

2nd Floor

6914 Sterling Oaks

Bedrooms: 5

Baths: 5-1/2

1st Floor: 4,385 sq ft

2nd Floor: 1,431 sq ft

Living Area: 5,816 sq ft

Width: 88'

Depth: 110'1"

Exterior Walls: 8" cbs

Foundation: Slab

Price Code: **PSE5**

Plan construction not available in Collier and Lee Counties, FL.

9

starwood

The repetition of graceful arches and elegant columns, stonework and a tile roof present an elegant facade for this stately Mediterranean-inspired home. The entry's dramatic barrel-vaulted ceiling begins a welcoming introduction; the foyer with its sweeping views of the scenery beyond the living room windows gives a warming embrace.

The casual areas of this home are to the left of the plan, including the leisure room, guest wing, and kitchen with its large island and pantry. An elegant gallery leads to two guest rooms, each with private full bathrooms and spacious walk-in closets.

The arches and columns from the facade add a flourish to interior spaces, defining boundaries between the open living room and dining room, creating a dramatic entry or a finishing touch to a niche.

A covered veranda rambles freely along the rear of this home, providing secluded areas for intimate conversation or larger gathering spots for grand soirees. A scenic backdrop for six rooms, this outdoor area is showcased through floor-to-ceiling windows, including curved walls of glass in the nook and living room, as well as French doors from the dining room and private study, and a sliding glass door from the master suite. Zero-corner sliding glass doors pocket into the walls of the leisure room, eliminating boundaries between outside and inside.

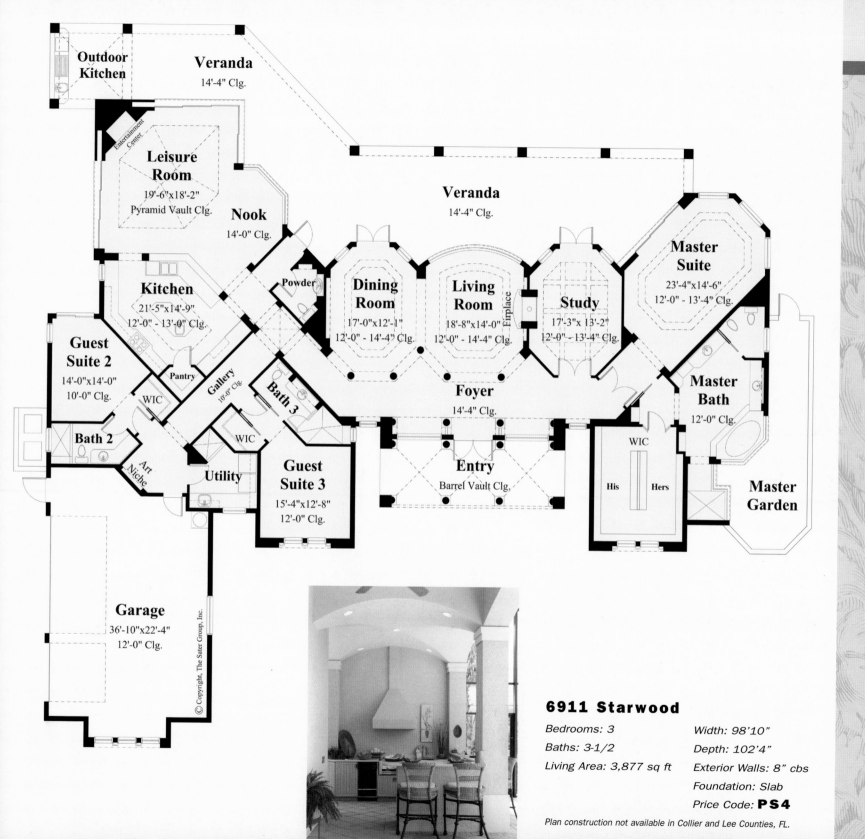

Outdoor Kitchen

Veranda
14'-4" Clg.

Leisure Room
19'-6"x18'-2"
Pyramid Vault Clg.

Nook
14'-0" Clg.

Veranda
14'-4" Clg.

Master Suite
23'-4"x14'-6"
12'-0" - 13'-4" Clg.

Entertainment Center

Kitchen
21'-5"x14'-9"
12'-0" - 13'-0" Clg.

Powder

Dining Room
17'-0"x12'-1"
12'-0" - 14'-4" Clg.

Living Room
18'-8"x14'-0"
12'-0" - 14'-4" Clg.

Fireplace

Study
17'-3"x 13'-2"
12'-0" - 13'-4" Clg.

Guest Suite 2
14'-0"x14'-0"
10'-0" Clg.

Pantry

WIC

Gallery
10'-0" Clg.

Bath 3

WIC

Master Bath
12'-0" Clg.

Bath 2

Art Niche

Utility

Guest Suite 3
15'-4"x12'-8"
12'-0" Clg.

Foyer
14'-4" Clg.

Entry
Barrel Vault Clg.

WIC

HIS   Hers

Master Garden

© Copyright, The Sater Group, Inc.

Garage
36'-10"x22'-4"
12'-0" Clg.

6911 Starwood

Bedrooms: 3

Baths: 3-1/2

Living Area: 3,877 sq ft

Width: 98'10"

Depth: 102'4"

Exterior Walls: 8" cbs

Foundation: Slab

Price Code: **PS4**

13

Plan construction not available in Collier and Lee Counties, FL.

autumn woods

The Italianate facade of this Florida style villa creates a Mediterranean allure. Light, views and open interior spaces expand the feel and flow of this 4,535 sq. ft. plan. Venture through double doors of the towering entry to find graceful columned arches defining the interior living spaces. Straight ahead, the corner pocket living room with multifaceted, cove-lit ceiling beckons with cozy comfort. To the left, an octagonal study is expanded by a vaulted ceiling and bay windows.

A pyramid-lit vaulted ceiling sets off the diamond-shaped leisure room shown at left.

The master suite is secluded to the left side of the plan for privacy, while guest quarters reside on the right, each with its own bath and walk-in closets. The island kitchen is conveniently open to the leisure room and breakfast nook. The back of the plan features views of the pool and patio area from every room.

Complemented by a rounded stepped ceiling, a curved glass sitting area in the master suite offers homeowners fantastic images. Ornate his-and-hers baths feature custom cabinetry and views of the wrap-around private garden.

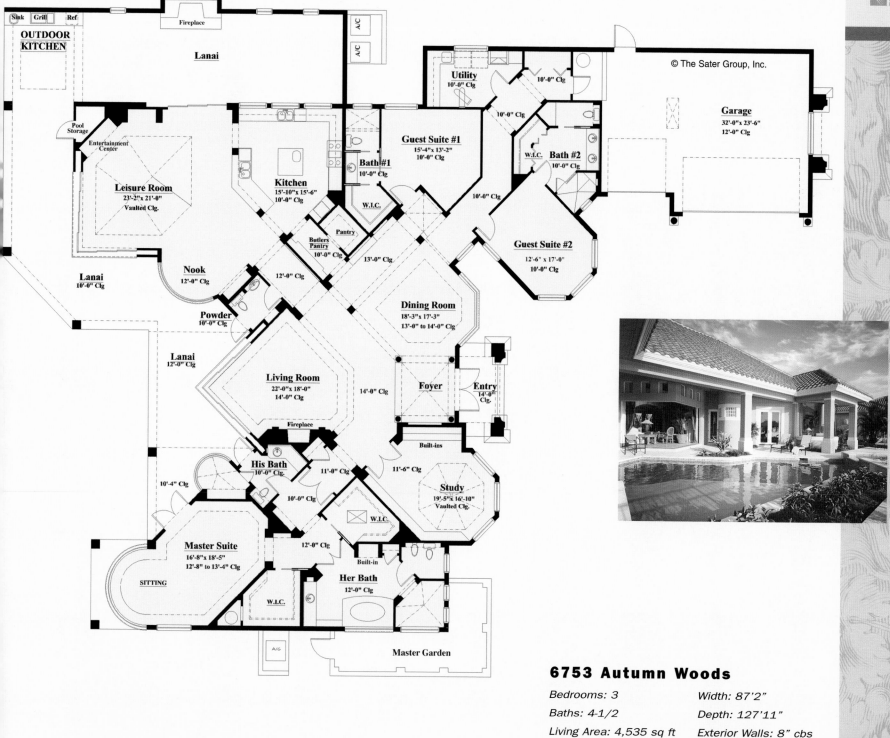

OUTDOOR KITCHEN

Sink | Grill | Ref

Fireplace

Lanai

A/C
A/C

Utility
10'-0" Clg

Garage
32'-0"x 23'-6"
12'-0" Clg

Pool Storage

Entertainment Center

10'-0" Clg

10'-0" Clg

Guest Suite #1
15'-4"x 13'-2"
10'-0" Clg

W.I.C.
Bath #2
10'-0" Clg

Leisure Room
23'-2"x 21'-0"
Vaulted Clg.

Kitchen
15'-10"x 15'-6"
10'-0" Clg

Bath #1
10'-0" Clg

W.I.C.

10'-0" Clg

Lanai
10'-0" Clg

Nook
12'-0" Clg

12'-0" Clg

Butlers Pantry
10'-0" Clg

Pantry

13'-0" Clg

Guest Suite #2
12'-6" x 17'-0"
10'-0" Clg

Powder
10'-0" Clg

Lanai
12'-0" Clg

Dining Room
18'-3"x 17'-3"
13'-0" to 14'-0" Clg

14'-0" Clg

Living Room
22'-0"x 18'-0"
14'-0" Clg

14'-0" Clg

Foyer

Entry
14'-0" Clg.

Fireplace

Built-ins

His Bath
10'-0" Clg

11'-0" Clg

11'-6" Clg

10'-4" Clg

10'-0" Clg

Study
19'-5"x 16'-10"
Vaulted Clg.

W.I.C.

Master Suite
16'-8" x 18'-5"
12'-8" to 13'-4" Clg

12'-0" Clg

Built-in

SITTING

W.I.C.

Her Bath
12'-0" Clg

A/C

Master Garden

6753 Autumn Woods

Bedrooms: 3

Baths: 4-1/2

Living Area: 4,535 sq ft

Width: 87'2"

Depth: 127'11"

Exterior Walls: 8" cbs

Foundation: Slab

Price Code: **PS8**

17

Plan construction not available in Collier and Lee Counties, FL.

st. regis grand

The great outdoors is enjoyed from a generously sized covered lanai that wraps around the rear and side of this home. Offering both covered and open-air sitting areas, an outdoor space off the island kitchen is warmed by a fireplace; a stone wall provides privacy and architectural interest.

This gourmet kitchen offers plenty of counter space, a second sink set into the island, and the added advantage of a view outside.

A lesson in geometry, the plan favors circles and octagons over more traditional square- or rectangular-shaped rooms. These free-flowing forms combine with an abundance of windows to create living environments that welcome in the outdoors and offer panoramic views.

Radius glass — some spanning floor to ceiling — embraces the home's nook and wraps the master suite's sitting area in windows. Circles add interest to showers in a guest room and one of the two master bathrooms, as well as the dining room. The study and two guest rooms assume more octagonal shapes, both enhanced by bay windows.

Vaulted ceilings in the leisure room, the second-floor media room and Bedroom 3, add a feeling of spaciousness and elegance.

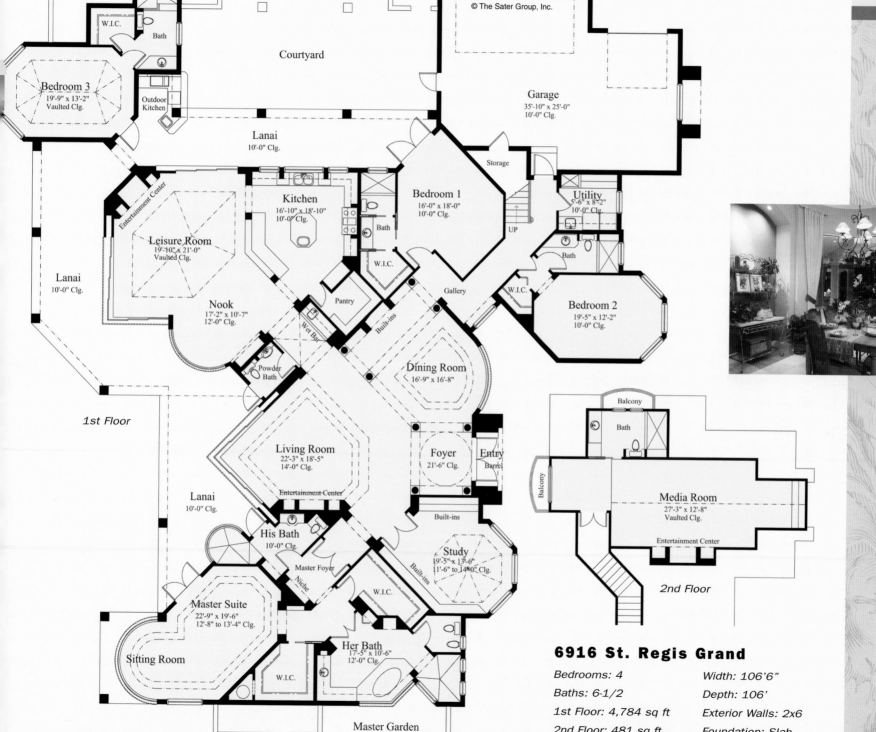

W.I.C.

Bath

Bedroom 3
19'-9" x 13'-2"
Vaulted Clg.

Outdoor
Kitchen

Courtyard

Fireplace

© The Sater Group, Inc.

Garage
35'-10" x 25'-0"
10'-0" Clg.

Lanai
10'-0" Clg.

Entertainment Center

Lanai
10'-0" Clg.

Leisure Room
19'-10" x 21'-0"
Vaulted Clg.

Kitchen
16'-10" x 18'-10"
10'-0" Clg.

Bath

Bedroom 1
16'-0" x 18'-0"
10'-0" Clg.

Storage

UP

Utility
5'-6" x 8'-2"
10'-0" Clg.

Bath

Nook
17'-2" x 10'-7"
12'-0" Clg.

Pantry

W.I.C.

Gallery

W.I.C.

Bedroom 2
19'-5" x 12'-2"
10'-0" Clg.

Wet Bar

Built-ins

Powder
Bath

Dining Room
16'-9" x 16'-8"

1st Floor

Lanai
10'-0" Clg.

Living Room
22'-3" x 18'-5"
14'-0" Clg.

Entertainment Center

Foyer
21'-6" Clg.

Entry

Barrel

Built-ins

Balcony

Bath

Balcony

Media Room
27'-3" x 12'-8"
Vaulted Clg.

Entertainment Center

His Bath
10'-0" Clg.

Master Foyer

Niche

Study
19'-5" x 13'-6"
11'-6" to 14'-0" Clg.

Built-ins

2nd Floor

Master Suite
22'-9" x 19'-6"
12'-8" to 13'-4" Clg.

W.I.C.

Sitting Room

Her Bath
17'-5" x 10'-6"
12'-0" Clg.

W.I.C.

Master Garden

6916 St. Regis Grand

Bedrooms: 4

Baths: 6-1/2

1st Floor: 4,784 sq ft

2nd Floor: 481 sq ft

Living Area: 5,265 sq ft

Width: 106'6"

Depth: 106'

Exterior Walls: 2x6

Foundation: Slab

Price Code: **PS8**

Plan construction not available in Collier and Lee Counties, FL.

monticello

Sunlight and moonlight filter into the foyer through glass walls that frame the entry door and showcase the lush landscaping surrounding the entry. This is the first hint at the importance of bringing the outside into this home. Straight ahead of the foyer, the corner of the living room is mere steps from the pool — a boundary that is erased with the opening of zero-corner sliding glass doors.

An elegant stepped ceiling, accented by moldings, lends a finishing touch to the living room. Columns offer decorative support to an archway that defines the space between the formal living room and dining room. The graceful scrollwork of a pair of custom-made iron gates of the wine grotto provides an eye-pleasing contrast to the cool colors and smooth textures of the gallery that leads to the kitchen, leisure room and guest rooms.
Wine grotto shown on page 25.

The open arrangement of the kitchen, leisure room and nook provides a continuum of space that is roomy, yet comfortable. The leisure room boasts an appealing corner fireplace, built-in entertainment center, pyramid ceiling and zero-corner doors, which open onto a special place off the lanai — an outdoor kitchen with bar seating.

The master suite encompasses a sitting area with bay window, two walk-in closets and a large bathroom with garden tub overlooking a private garden spot — a soulful sojourn for lucky homeowners.

A butler's pantry is cleverly accessible to both dining room and kitchen, as is a grotto, which is ideally situated for a wine cellar. A groin-vaulted ceiling and wrought-iron gates create a quaint setting for storing favorite vintages.

Outdoor Kitchen

Leisure Room
21'-10" x 16'-0"
Pyramid Clg.

Fireplace

Entertainment Center

Desk

Kitchen
15'-8" x 17'-5"
11'-0" - 12'-0" Clg.

Bedroom 2
13'-2" x 14'-2"
10'-0" Clg.

Bath 2

W.I.C.

Utility
7'-2" x 14'-2"
10'-0" Clg.

Garage
35'-2" x 22'-8"
12'-0" Clg.

© Copyright, The Sater Group, Inc.

Lanai
12'-0" Clg.

Nook
10'-0" x 11'-0"
12'-0" Clg.

Pantry

Butlers

W.I.C.

Grotto
Groin Vault Clg.

Bath 3

Bedroom 3
13'-0" x 16'-6"
10'-0" Clg.

Powder Bath

Dining Room
18'-1" x 14'-0"
14'-0" - 16'-0" Clg.

Lanai
12'-0" Clg.

Living Room
22'-1" x 17'-6"
14'-0" - 16'-0" Clg.

Foyer
Barrel Vault Clg.

Entry
Barrel Vault Clg.

Lanai
12'-0" Clg.

Study
16'-4" x 13'-0"
14'-0" x 15'-0" Clg.

Niche

W.I.C.

Master Foyer
11'-6" x 12'-0" Clg.

Niche

Master Bath
12'-0" Clg.

Master Garden

Sitting
11'-8" x 10'-0"
12'-0" - 13'-0" Clg.

Master Suite
17'-10" x 14'-4"
12'-0" - 14'-0" Clg.

W.I.C.

Linen

6907 Monticello

Bedrooms: 3

Baths: 3-1/2

Living Area: 4,255 sq ft

Width: 91'6"

Depth: 117'

Exterior Walls: 8" cbs

Foundation: Slab

Price Code: **PSE3**

Plan construction not available in Collier and Lee Counties, FL.

lindley

A barrel-tile roof, graceful arches, rope columns and stone accents impart a distinctively Mediterranean flavor to the exterior of this home. Dramatic stepped ceilings are introduced in the foyer and are repeated in the living room, throughout the master suite and kitchen. The gracious living room is showcased from the foyer, much like a fine work of art.

Rope columns lend a touch of formality to the more casual areas of the plan, adding architectural interest to spaces that define the boundaries between the kitchen, nook and leisure room. Arches also accentuate doorways and provide space for a wet bar.

Water features have been designed into this plan, with the pool gently lapping at the arched windows in the living room and a koi pond providing the scenic backdrop for a piano bar to the left.

In the leisure room, arched wall niches provide built-in space for an entertainment center, as well as plenty of display space. A pyramid ceiling with wood beams and a fireplace setting outside on the lanai add a warmth that is reminiscent of a northern ski lodge.

Additional ceiling interest is found in the master bathroom where circles echo the form of a round tub; in the dining room and study, both of which boast cove ceilings; and on the lanai, where a pyramid ceiling caps the outdoor kitchen.

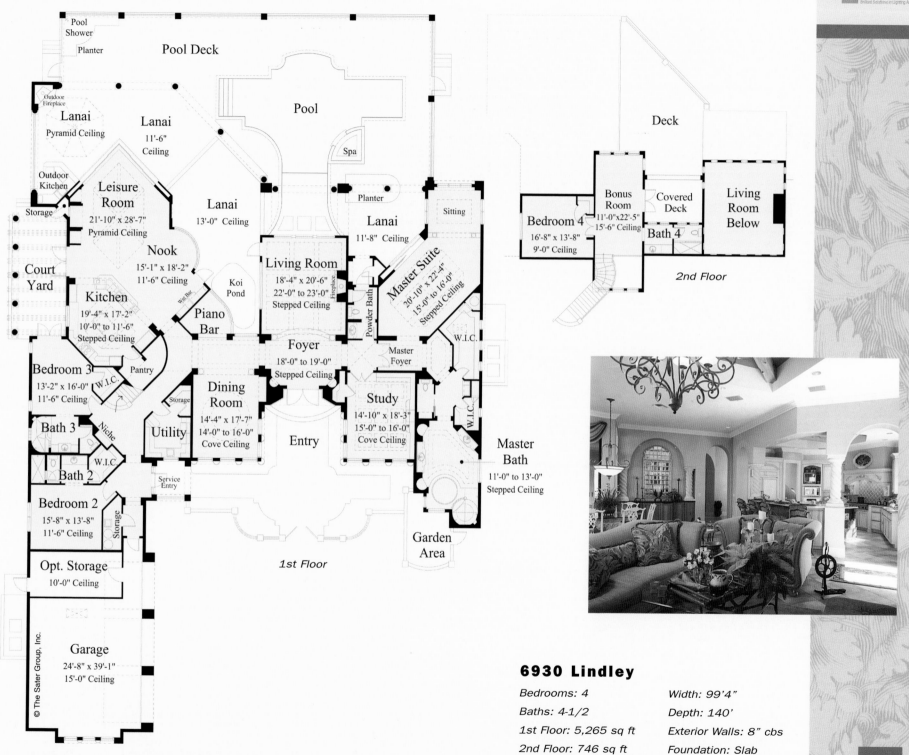

1st Floor

Pool Shower
Planter
Pool Deck
Outdoor Fireplace
Planter
Lanai
Pyramid Ceiling
Lanai
11'-6" Ceiling
Pool
Spa
Outdoor Kitchen
Storage
Leisure Room
21'-10" x 28'-7"
Pyramid Ceiling
Lanai
13'-0" Ceiling
Planter
Sitting
Nook
15'-1" x 18'-2"
11'-6" Ceiling
Lanai
11'-8" Ceiling
Court Yard
Koi Pond
Living Room
18'-4" x 20'-6"
22'-0" to 23'-0"
Stepped Ceiling
Master Suite
20'-10" x 22'-4"
15'-0" to 16'-0"
Stepped Ceiling
Kitchen
19'-4" x 17'-2"
10'-0" to 11'-6"
Stepped Ceiling
Wet Bar
Piano Bar
Fireplace
Powder Bath
W.I.C.
Bedroom 3
13'-2" x 16'-0"
11'-6" Ceiling
W.I.C.
Pantry
Foyer
18'-0" to 19'-0"
Stepped Ceiling
Master Foyer
W.I.C.
Bath 3
Niche
W.I.C.
Storage
Utility
Dining Room
14'-4" x 17'-7"
14'-0" to 16'-0"
Cove Ceiling
Study
14'-10" x 18'-3"
15'-0" to 16'-0"
Cove Ceiling
W.I.C.
Bath 2
Entry
Master Bath
11'-0" to 13'-0"
Stepped Ceiling
Bedroom 2
15'-8" x 13'-8"
11'-6" Ceiling
Storage
Service Entry
Opt. Storage
10'-0" Ceiling
Garden Area

© The Sater Group, Inc.

Garage
24'-8" x 39'-1"
15'-0" Ceiling

2nd Floor

Deck
Bonus Room
11'-0"x22'-5"
15'-6" Ceiling
Covered Deck
Living Room Below
Bedroom 4
16'-8" x 13'-8"
9'-0" Ceiling
Bath 4

6930 Lindley

Bedrooms: 4

Baths: 4-1/2

1st Floor: 5,265 sq ft

2nd Floor: 746 sq ft

Living Area: 6,011 sq ft

Width: 99'4"

Depth: 140'

Exterior Walls: 8" cbs

Foundation: Slab

Price Code: **PSE6**

Plan construction not available in Collier and Lee Counties, FL.

esmerelda court

The facade foreshadows the importance of windows in the design of this two-story home. Large windows with transoms frame the entry, whose gentle arch is repeated in the shapes of other windows. Inside, a garden tub in the master bathroom enjoys a window wall overlooking a private garden, and the leisure room opens onto a covered lanai via zero-corner sliding glass doors. A trio of floor-to-ceiling windows in the living room gaze onto the covered lanai.

The stepped ceiling in the study assumes a wagon-wheel design — a geometry that is complemented by the squares and rectangles of large vertical windows capped by transom windows. Space flows effortlessly between the dining room and living room, where boundaries are subtly defined by architectural elements such as columns, arches and stepped ceilings.

Spectacular ceilings add a degree of sophistication throughout the home. Each rooms unique treatment add character and warmth to its spaciousness.

Kitchen comforts include a large center island, plenty of cabinet and counter space, a menu desk for planning gourmet meals, and pull-up counter seating.

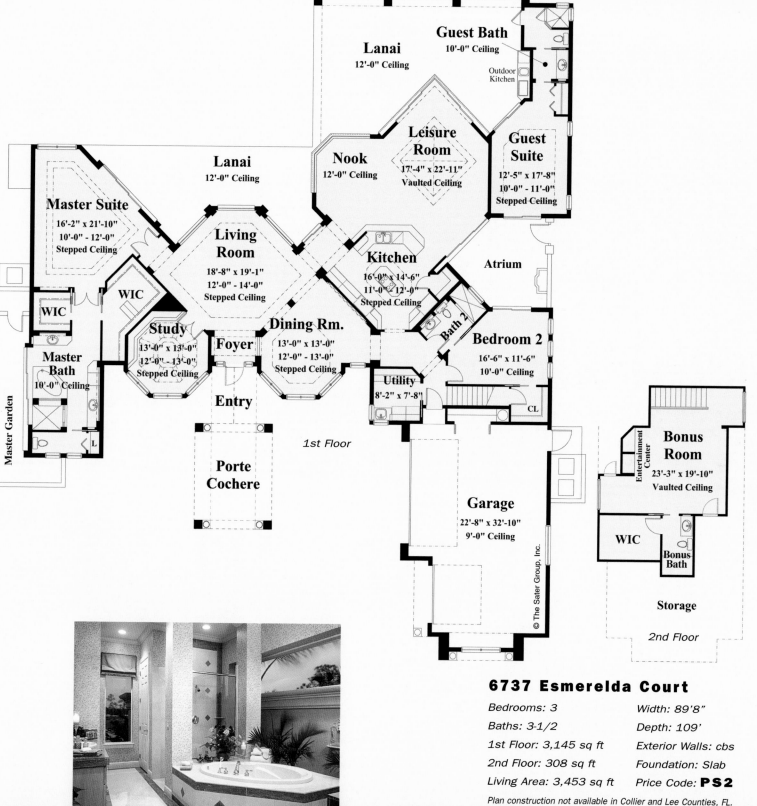

Lanai
12'-0" Ceiling

Guest Bath
10'-0" Ceiling

Outdoor Kitchen

Leisure Room
17'-4" x 22'-11"
Vaulted Ceiling

Nook
12'-0" Ceiling

Guest Suite
12'-5" x 17'-8"
10'-0" - 11'-0"
Stepped Ceiling

Lanai
12'-0" Ceiling

Master Suite
16'-2" x 21'-10"
10'-0" - 12'-0"
Stepped Ceiling

Living Room
18'-8" x 19'-1"
12'-0" - 14'-0"
Stepped Ceiling

Kitchen
16'-0" x 14'-6"
11'-0" - 12'-0"
Stepped Ceiling

Atrium

WIC

WIC

Study
13'-0" x 13'-0"
12'-0" - 13'-0"
Stepped Ceiling

Foyer

Dining Rm.
13'-0" x 13'-0"
12'-0" - 13'-0"
Stepped Ceiling

Bath 2

Bedroom 2
16'-6" x 11'-6"
10'-0" Ceiling

Master Bath
10'-0" Ceiling

Utility
8'-2" x 7'-8"

CL

Entry

Master Garden

L

Porte Cochere

1st Floor

Garage
22'-8" x 32'-10"
9'-0" Ceiling

© The Sater Group, Inc.

Entertainment Center

Bonus Room
23'-3" x 19'-10"
Vaulted Ceiling

WIC

Bonus Bath

Storage

2nd Floor

LiteTouch
Brilliant Solutions in Lighting Automation

6737 Esmerelda Court

Bedrooms: 3   Width: 89'8"

Baths: 3-1/2   Depth: 109'

1st Floor: 3,145 sq ft   Exterior Walls: cbs

2nd Floor: 308 sq ft   Foundation: Slab

Living Area: 3,453 sq ft   Price Code: **PS2**

Plan construction not available in Collier and Lee Counties, FL.

sherbrooke

This spectacular home has a unique Mediterranean facade and is full of amenities. Upon entering, the flawless detail is apparent with gracious marble floors, stone columns and breathtaking ceilings trimmed with exotic wood. Formal spaces and the lanai are immediately visible upon entering the foyer. Recessed paneled columns with slumped arches and crown moulding separate spacious living and dining areas. The living room, directly in front of the entry, has an extended mantel with art niche and looks out to the patio.

A high domed ceiling trimmed in cypress wood crowns the formal dining room, with built-in china cabinet. The abundant use of wood adds a touch of old world charm throughout.

A powder bath off the lanai is accentuated by a Romanesque arch and creative use of crown molding.

Off to the right of the foyer is the master bedroom suite with lavish styling, huge spacious walk-in closets and pampering master bath. It features an oversized Roman tub and an open shower with a tranquil garden view.

Perfect for entertaining, the patio has an outdoor kitchen and a marvelous pool with splendid waterfall.

The leisure room shown on pag 37 offers outdoor views of both the lanai and the courtyard, alc with built-ins and a wet-bar. The courtyard's fireplace creates th perfect setting for a cozy eveni get-together.

© The Sater Group, Inc.

Guest Suite 2
15'-4" x 13'-6"
10'-8" Clg.

Bath 2

L UP DN.

Bar

Courtyard
20'-4" x 14'-8"

Fireplace

Guest Suite 1
13'-0" x 14'-8"
10'-0" Clg.

Bath 1

W.I.C.

Garage
32'-0" x 22'-8"
11'-0" Clg.

W.I.C.

Outdoor Grill

Lanai
10'-8" Clg.

Entertainment
Center

Leisure Room
20'-4" x 19'-9"
10'-8" Clg.

Kitchen
16'-11" x 20'-4"
9'-0" to 10'-0" Clg.

Pantry

Desk

Utility
11'-4" x 7'-0"
12'-0" Clg.

Lanai
Vaulted Clg.

Nook
10'-8" Clg.

Groin
Vaults

Dining
16'-7" x 17'-9"
15'-0" to 16'-4" Clg.

Powder &
Cabana Bath

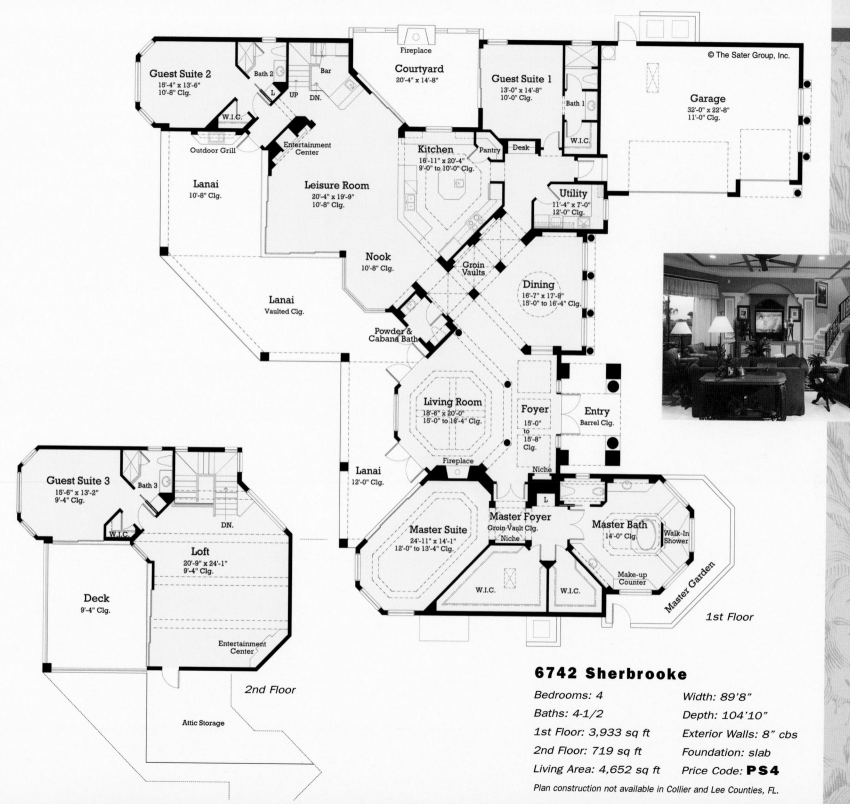

Living Room
18'-6" x 20'-0"
15'-0" to 16'-4" Clg.

Foyer
15'-0"
to
15'-8"

Entry
Barrel Clg.

Guest Suite 3
15'-6" x 13'-2"
9'-4" Clg.

Bath 3

DN.

W.I.C.

Fireplace

Niche

Lanai
12'-0" Clg.

L

Loft
20'-9" x 24'-1"
9'-4" Clg.

Deck
9'-4" Clg.

Master Suite
24'-11" x 14'-1"
12'-0" to 13'-4" Clg.

Master Foyer
Groin Vault Clg.

Niche

Master Bath
14'-0" Clg.

Walk-In
Shower

W.I.C.

W.I.C.

Make-up
Counter

Master Garden

Entertainment
Center

Attic Storage

2nd Floor

1st Floor

6742 Sherbrooke

Bedrooms: 4

Baths: 4-1/2

1st Floor: 3,933 sq ft

2nd Floor: 719 sq ft

Living Area: 4,652 sq ft

Width: 89'8"

Depth: 104'10"

Exterior Walls: 8" cbs

Foundation: slab

Price Code: **PS4**

Plan construction not available in Collier and Lee Counties, FL.

prestonwood

Serving as a regal crown, this home's signature feature is its captivating two-story rotunda. Double doors open to reveal the most breathtaking area of the home —a circular grand hall into which natural light flows. Ringed-in columns support the rotunda and spectacular 36-foot-high ceiling. A formal garden with refreshing water feature extends the view off one side, while opposite, an elegant curving staircase leads to the guest suites and a sitting loft with balcony.

The grand hall makes a smooth transition to the formal salon tucked beneath the second-story balcony. The main living area is contained in two wings off the grand hall and flanks the generous veranda, granting spectacular views from virtually everywhere.

This master bath is simply unforgettable. Its magnificent tub and sunken shower take center stage. Simple square towers break up the shower and bath area, and make the room feel grand in size. A tray cove-lit ceiling sparkles soft ambient light.

Majestic columns stand just feet away from an inviting pool and spa in the back of the home. The outdoor patio boasts a fireplace (shown next page) and outdoor kitchen — perfect for social gatherings.

The gourmet kitchen is a well-organized culinary paradise, providing a cooktop island and walk-in pantry.

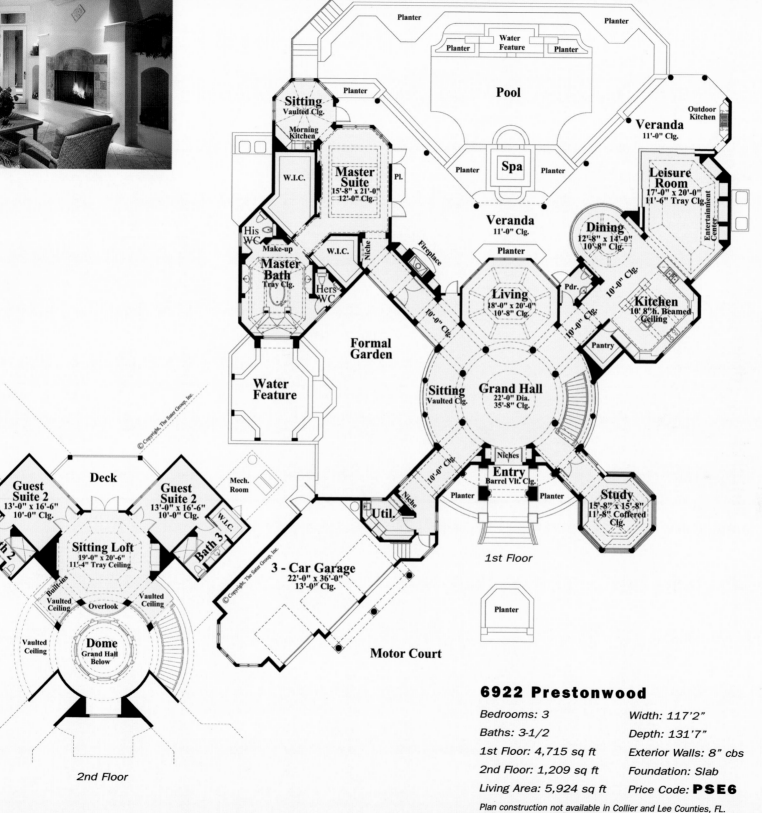

Planter Planter

Pool

Planter

Sitting
Vaulted Clg.

Morning Kitchen

W.I.C.

Master Suite
15'-8" x 21'-0"
12'-0" Clg.

Pl.

Water Feature

Planter Planter

Spa

Planter Planter

Veranda
11'-0" Clg.

Outdoor Kitchen

His WC

Make-up

W.I.C.

Niche

Planter

Leisure Room
17'-0" x 20'-0"
11'-6" Tray Clg.

Entertainment Center

Master Bath
Tray Clg.

Hers WC

Fireplace

Dining
12'-8" x 14'-0"
10'-8" Clg.

Veranda
11'-0" Clg.

Pdr.

10'-0" Clg.

Living
18'-0" x 20'-0"
10'-8" Clg.

10'-0" Clg.

Kitchen
10' 8"h. Beamed Ceiling

Formal Garden

Pantry

Water Feature

Sitting
Vaulted Clg.

Grand Hall
22'-0" Dia.
35'-8" Clg.

Niches

10'-0" Clg.

Entry
Barrel Vlt. Clg.

Planter Planter

Study
15'-8" x 15'-8"
11'-8" Coffered Clg.

Niche

© Copyright, The Sater Group, Inc.

Deck

Mech. Room

Guest Suite 2
13'-0" x 16'-6"
10'-0" Clg.

W.I.C.

Bath 2

Sitting Loft
19'-0" x 20'-6"
11'-4" Tray Ceiling

Guest Suite 2
13'-0" x 16'-6"
10'-0" Clg.

Mech. Room

W.I.C.

Bath 3

Built-ins

Vaulted Ceiling

Overlook

Vaulted Ceiling

Vaulted Ceiling

Dome
Grand Hall Below

Vaulted Ceiling

© Copyright, The Sater Group, Inc.

3 - Car Garage
22'-0" x 36'-0"
13'-0" Clg.

Util.

Motor Court

Planter

1st Floor

2nd Floor

6922 Prestonwood

Bedrooms: 3

Baths: 3-1/2

1st Floor: 4,715 sq ft

2nd Floor: 1,209 sq ft

Living Area: 5,924 sq ft

Width: 117'2"

Depth: 131'7"

Exterior Walls: 8" cbs

Foundation: Slab

Price Code: **PSE6**

Plan construction not available in Collier and Lee Counties, FL.

LiteTouch
Brilliant Solutions in Lighting Automation

41

andros island

British Colonial inspiration reminiscent of the Caribbean is seen in the facade of this home with it shutters, cupola and bay windows in the dining room, study and guest suite. The importance of windows become evident inside, where a large lanai and courtyard provide the backdrop for zero-corner sliding glass doors in the living room and leisure room, curved glass in the nook, and a large sittting room in the master suite, which is virtually surrounded by windows. Windows in a walk-in shower overlook a private garden.

Close your eyes and imagine snuggling up to a roaring fire, with the benefit of being outside to enjoy the gentle chirp of crickets and the soothing rustle of a soft breeze. This cozy scenario becomes reality in this home's courtyard, where an outdoor kitchen and dining area extend the possibilities.

Ideal for a casual dinner party or a quiet night with your significant other, this outdoor space continues into a lanai that meanders along the rear of the home, creating all sorts of retreats.

Zero-corner sliding glass doors in the leisure room and living room open onto the lanai. A built-in entertainment center is set into the corner of the leisure room, where space flows freely with the kitchen and nook.

This casual area of the home enjoys access to both the courtyard and lanai. Custom built-ins encircle the study, appeasing those eager to display a generous collection of literature or works of art. Another built-in — a buffet — is found in the dining room.

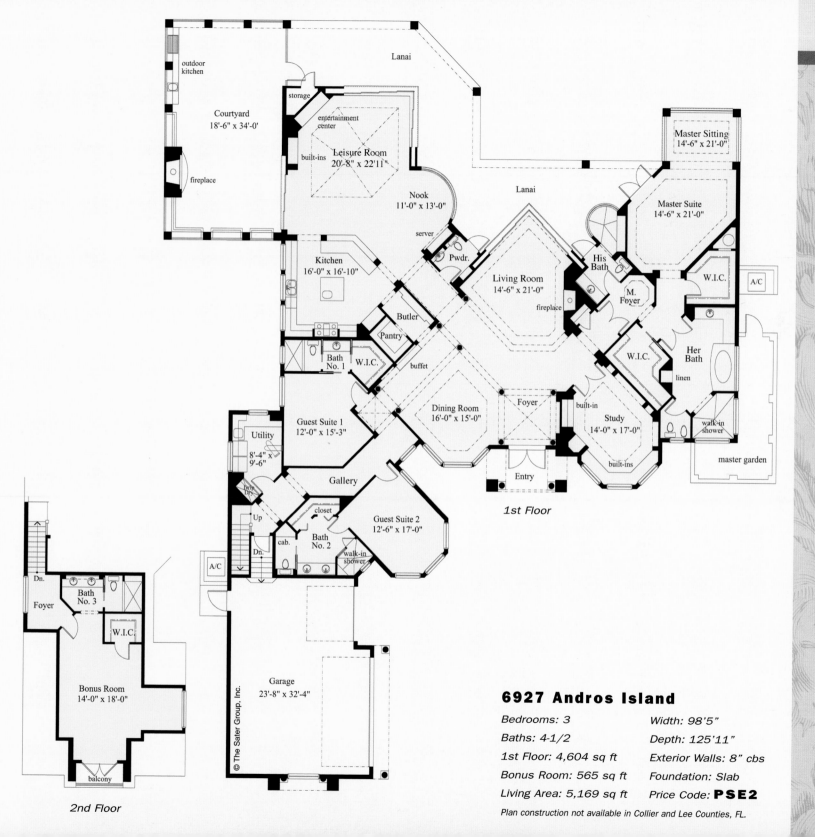

Courtyard
18'-6" x 34'-0"

outdoor kitchen

fireplace

Lanai

storage

entertainment center

built-ins

Leisure Room
20'-8" x 22'11"

Nook
11'-0" x 13'-0"

Lanai

server

Master Sitting
14'-6" x 21'-0"

Master Suite
14'-6" x 21'-0"

Kitchen
16'-0" x 16'-10"

Pwdr.

Living Room
14'-6" x 21'-0"

fireplace

His Bath

M. Foyer

W.I.C.

A/C

Butler

Pantry

Bath No. 1

W.I.C.

buffet

W.I.C.

Her Bath

linen

walk-in shower

Guest Suite 1
12'-0" x 15'-3"

Utility
8'-4" x 9'-6"

Dining Room
16'-0" x 15'-0"

Foyer

built-in

Study
14'-0" x 17'-0"

built-ins

master garden

Gallery

pwdr.

closet

Up

cab.

Dn.

Bath No. 2

walk-in shower

Guest Suite 2
12'-6" x 17'-0"

Entry

1st Floor

Dn.

Foyer

Bath No. 3

W.I.C.

A/C

Bonus Room
14'-0" x 18'-0"

© The Sater Group, Inc.

Garage
23'-8" x 32'-4"

balcony

2nd Floor

6927 Andros Island

Bedrooms: 3

Baths: 4-1/2

1st Floor: 4,604 sq ft

Bonus Room: 565 sq ft

Living Area: 5,169 sq ft

Width: 98'5"

Depth: 125'11"

Exterior Walls: 8" cbs

Foundation: Slab

Price Code: **PSE2**

Plan construction not available in Collier and Lee Counties, FL.

saraceno

Arches and simple lines dominate the classic architecture of this home with corbels, banding, and hipped roofs providing visual excitement. Inside, a thoughtful plan arranges social areas and guest rooms to the left and the master suite and study to the right.

Private pockets of gathering areas are created by the gentle movement of the home's rear elevation, while a different perspective is experienced from the second-floor deck.

Designed to celebrate outdoor living and the views from inside, the rear elevation of this home is punctuated heavily by windows and sliding glass doors. Large windows provide wide-open views of the home's surroundings, while sliding glass doors extend the space, often serving to bring the outside in.

Designed for entertaining, an open floor plan between living room and dining room allows a wet bar to serve as the staging area for refreshments and hors d'oeuvres. Boundaries between these spaces are subtly defined by columns and changing ceilings.

Natural light streams into the leisure room through zero-corner sliding glass doors and a second-story band of vertical windows, opening up this room to the outdoors. This drama is heightened by a 22-foot coffered ceiling. A second-floor loft overlooks the leisure room, and provides a private retreat for the fourth bedroom.

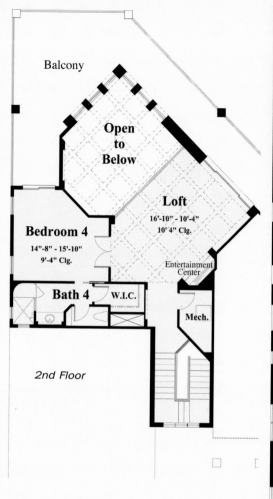

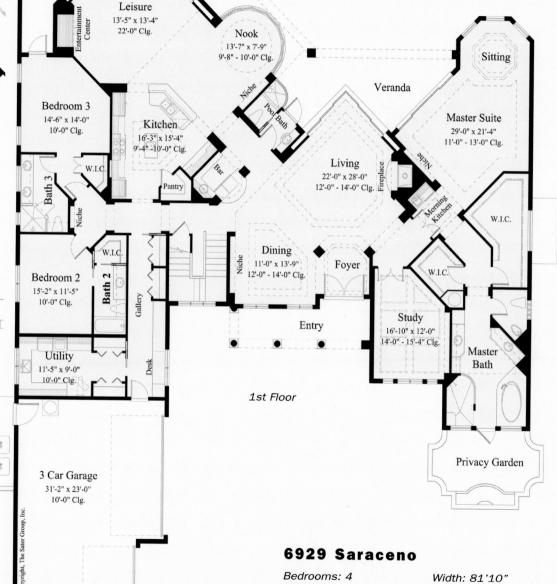

Balcony

Open to Below

Loft
16'-10" - 10'-4"
10' 4" Clg.

Bedroom 4
14"-8" - 15'-10"
9'-4" Clg.

Entertainment Center

Bath 4   W.I.C.

Mech.

2nd Floor

Veranda

Outdoor Kitchen

Entertainment Center

Leisure
13'-5" x 13'-4"
22'-0" Clg.

Nook
13'-7" x 7'-9"
9'-8" - 10'-0" Clg.

Sitting

Veranda

Master Suite
29'-0" x 21'-4"
11'-0" - 13'-0" Clg.

Bedroom 3
14'-6" x 14'-0"
10'-0" Clg.

Kitchen
16'-3" x 15'-4"
9'-4" -10'-0" Clg.

Niche

Pool Bath

Bath 3

W.I.C.

Niche

Bar

Pantry

Living
22'-0" x 28'-0"
12'-0" - 14'-0" Clg.

Fireplace

Niche

Morning Kitchen

W.I.C.

Bedroom 2
15'-2" x 11'-5"
10'-0" Clg.

Bath 2

W.I.C.

Gallery

Niche

Dining
11'-0" x 13'-9"
12'-0" - 14'-0" Clg.

Foyer

W.I.C.

Desk

Entry

Study
16'-10" x 12'-0"
14'-0" - 15'-4" Clg.

Master Bath

Utility
11'-5" x 9'-0"
10'-0" Clg.

1st Floor

3 Car Garage
31'-2" x 23'-0"
10'-0" Clg.

Privacy Garden

© Copyright, The Sater Group, Inc.

Ceilings are elevated to an art form with dramatic treatments like trays and coffers taking on various geometric shapes — a circle in the breakfast nook, an octagon in the sitting area in the master suite, and crisp squares formed by the beams in the leisure room. Rope lighting and recessed lighting enhance the effect.

6929 Saraceno

Bedrooms: 4

Baths: 5

1st Floor: 4,137 sq ft

2nd Floor: 876 sq ft

Living Area: 5,013 sq ft

Width: 81'10"

Depth: 113'

Exterior Walls: 8" cbs

Foundation: Slab

Price Code: **PS8**

Plan construction not available in Collier and Lee Counties, FL.

LiteTouch
Brilliant Solutions in Lighting Automation

colony bay

Turrets, pitched roofs, arches and corbel accents gently kiss the facade in subtle British Colonial undertones. The plan is designed to revel in outdoor living with a courtyard and covered lanai that beckon to be indulged. Rooms open onto these outdoor spaces through floor-to-ceiling windows and zero-corner doors that eliminate walls in the living and leisure rooms.

The covered courtyard will become a favorite gathering spot. Large enough to accommodate an outdoor kitchen and grill, fireplace and dining for six, this space is cozy enough to enjoy engaging intimate fireside conversation or a casual dinner party for your closest friends.

Zero-corner sliding glass doors expand entertainment options by extending the living room and leisure room to a covered lanai that winds its way along the back of the home. Curved glass expands spaces in the nook off the island kitchen and in the shower in his bathroom in the master bedroom.

Windows also become an important element in a sitting area in the master bedroom, from the garden tub overlooking a private garden, in the study, as well as in the dining room and one of the home's two guest bedrooms.

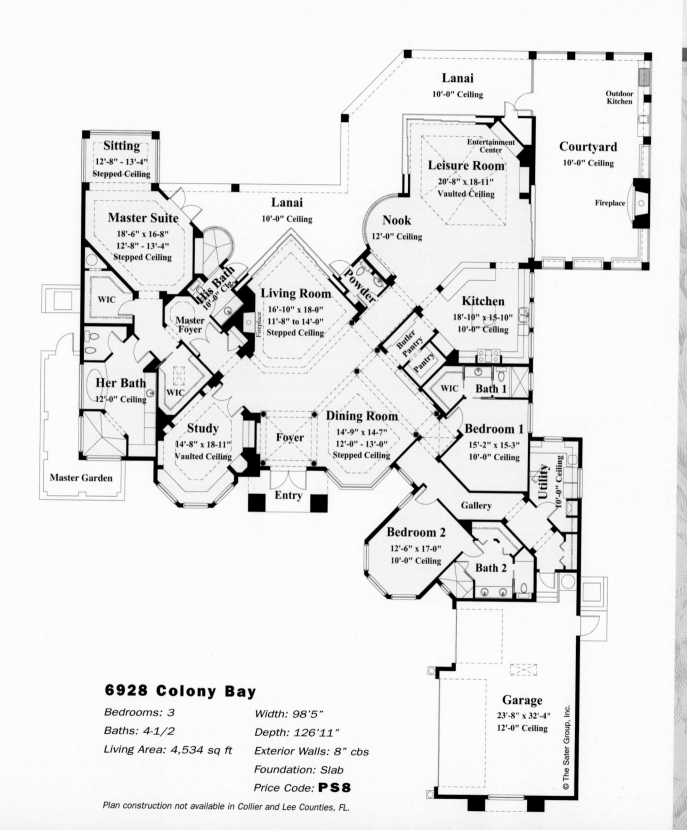

Lanai
10'-0" Ceiling

Outdoor Kitchen

Courtyard
10'-0" Ceiling

Fireplace

Entertainment Center

Leisure Room
20'-8" x 18-11"
Vaulted Ceiling

Sitting
12'-8" - 13'-4"
Stepped Ceiling

Lanai
10'-0" Ceiling

Nook
12'-0" Ceiling

Master Suite
18'-6" x 16-8"
12'-8" - 13'-4"
Stepped Ceiling

WIC

His Bath
10'-0" Clg.

Master Foyer

Living Room
16'-10" x 18-0"
11'-8" to 14'-0"
Stepped Ceiling

Powder

Fireplace

Kitchen
18'-10" x 15-10"
10'-0" Ceiling

Butler Pantry

Pantry

WIC

Bath 1

Her Bath
12'-0" Ceiling

WIC

Study
14'-8" x 18-11"
Vaulted Ceiling

Foyer

Dining Room
14'-9" x 14-7"
12'-0" - 13'-0"
Stepped Ceiling

Bedroom 1
15'-2" x 15-3"
10'-0" Ceiling

Utility
10'-0" Ceiling

Master Garden

Entry

Gallery

Bedroom 2
12'-6" x 17-0"
10'-0" Ceiling

Bath 2

6928 Colony Bay

Bedrooms: 3

Baths: 4-1/2

Living Area: 4,534 sq ft

Width: 98'5"

Depth: 126'11"

Exterior Walls: 8" cbs

Foundation: Slab

Price Code: **PS8**

Garage
23'-8" x 32'-4"
12'-0" Ceiling

© The Sater Group, Inc.

Plan construction not available in Collier and Lee Counties, FL.

huntington lakes

Barrel dormer's and cupola add architectural interest to this home, which offers Southern contemporary inspirations through the use of columns, arches, stone ornamentation and porte-cochere. Double doors open onto a bowed foyer, which introduces guests to the living room immediately ahead.

The living room's two-sided fireplace is shared by the adjoining study, and sliding glass doors pocket into the wall, opening up the room to a generously sized covered lanai.

The lanai embraces the rear of the home, wrapping around to the leisure room, where zero-corner sliding glass doors open up two corners — an effect that pushes the room outside.

Interesting ceilings throughout the home add elegance, visual interest and excitement. Stepped ceilings punctuate the living room, master bedroom and dining room. Dramatic pyramid vaulted ceilings are used in the leisure room and repeated in the outdoor kitchen area of the lanai.

lanai
20'-8" x 10'-0" avg.

lanai
42'-0" x 10'-0" avg.

sitting
fireplace

master
16'-8" x 23'-10"
step clg.

nook
10'-0" x 12'-0" avg.
14'-0" clg.

enter.
center

leisure
27'-0" x 29'-0" avg.
pyramid vault clg.

study
14'-0" x 15'-6"
17'-8" clg.

living
18'-2" x 21'-2" avg.
step clg.

tv
niche

his

hers

2 sided
fireplace

built
ins

gallery

lanai
20'-0" x 20'-0" avg.
pyramid vault clg.

pantry

wetbar

gallery

dressing

his w/c

fireplace

outdoor
kitchen

kitchen
20'-6" x 14'7"
14'-0" clg.

foyer

stor.

make up

her w/c

master bath

guest
18'-0" x 14'-8"
10'-0" clg.

stor.

up

dining
15'-4" x 18'-0"
step clg.

entry

hers

his

utility

1st Floor

porte cochere
14'-0" clg.

private
garden

© The Sater Group, Inc.

garage
24'-8" x 25'-4"

deck
20'-0" x 11'-0" avg.

retreat
16'-4" x 23'-0" avg.
step clg.

dn.

wetbar

built
ins

garage
22'-0" x 15'-0" avg.

storage

mechanical
storage

guest
18'-0" x 14'-8"
tray clg.

down

cedar
closet

© The Sater Group, Inc.

2nd Floor

wetbar

media
27'-0" x 21'-10"
vaulted clg.

entertainment
center

To the right of the plan, a
gallery leads to the private
master suite, which enjoys a
fireplace and picturesque
views of the lanai and in the
front of the home, a private
garden, seen from the shower.

6900 Huntington Lakes

Bedrooms: 3

Baths: 4

1st Floor: 5,170 sq ft

2nd Floor: 1,600 sq ft

Living Area: 6,770 sq ft

Width: 140'7"

Depth: 118'4"

Exterior Walls: 8" cbs

Foundation: Slab

Price Code: **PSE8**

Plan construction not available in Collier and Lee Counties, FL.

sunningdale cove

This truly unique courtyard design brings outdoor living inside. The home is wrapped around a central pool area and helps provide optimum privacy while creating great views from the living areas. A covered portico entry way opens to reveal the courtyard and warmly welcomes you into the exciting area.

The outdoor courtyard area can be built with or without the pool and spa depending on your needs or region. If the pool is not used, the outdoor space can be a wonderful garden or porch area.

The main entry door opens to the two-story grand salon and glass to the rear views. The salon has a bayed shape to the rear yard while the coffered ceiling adds drama to the space. The formal dining room is off the grand salon area and also faces the rear yard. A staircase graces the right foyer and leads to the upstairs bedrooms.

The family areas have a great view of the pool and courtyard area. The leisure room has a high ceiling, an entertainment center and glass doors to a covered poolside lanai.

An outdoor fireplace makes gathering at the covered lanai an enjoyable experience. The high ceiling allows for natural light and cooling breezes at the lanai area.

A detached guesthouse has a pool bath area and a grill space. This area is perfect for guests, a cabana, game room, home office or whatever you may desire. The guesthouse allows the pool to remain a private space by blocking the courtyard from the front entry area.

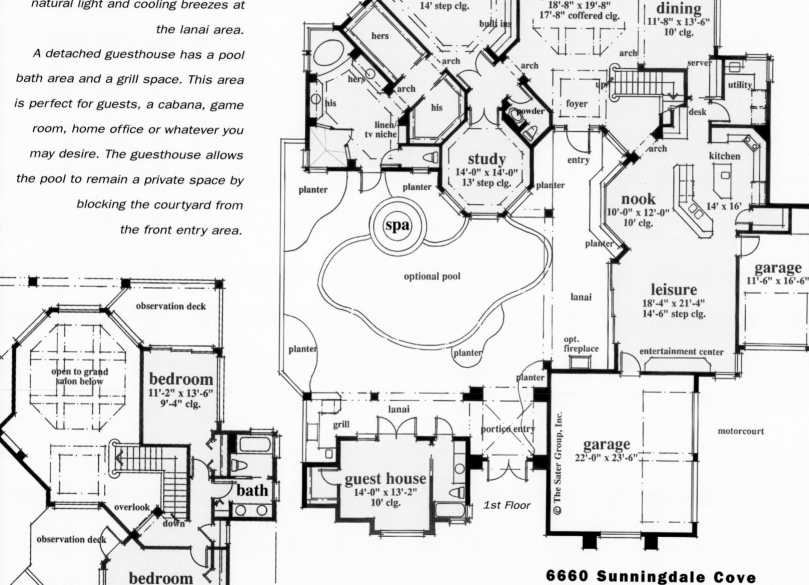

master
20'-4" x 22'-0"
14' step clg.

grand salon
18'-8" x 19'-8"
17'-8" coffered clg.

dining
11'-8" x 13'-6"
10' clg.

lanai

built ins

hers

hers

his

his

arch

arch

arch

arch

server

utility

linen/
tv niche

powder

foyer

up

desk

kitchen
14' x 16'

study
14'-0" x 14'-0"
13' step clg.

entry

arch

nook
10'-0" x 12'-0"
10' clg.

planter

planter

planter

planter

planter

spa

optional pool

planter

lanai

garage
11'-6" x 16'-6"

leisure
18'-4" x 21'-4"
14'-6" step clg.

opt.
fireplace

entertainment center

planter

planter

grill

lanai

portico entry

motorcourt

© The Sater Group, Inc.

guest house
14'-0" x 13'-2"
10' clg.

garage
22'-0" x 23'-6"

1st Floor

observation deck

open to grand
salon below

bedroom
11'-2" x 13'-6"
9'-4" clg.

overlook

down

bath

observation deck

bedroom
15'-2" x 11'-8"
9'-4" clg.

2nd Floor

6660 Sunningdale Cove

Bedrooms: 4

Baths: 3-1/2

1st Floor: 2,853 sq ft

2nd Floor: 627 sq ft

Guest House: 312 sq ft

Living Area: 3,792 sq ft

Width: 80'

Depth: 96'

Exterior Walls: 8" cbs

Foundation: Slab

Price Code: **C3**

monterrey lane

This home skillfully blends a somewhat formal design with the warmth and texture of Mediterranean style. Spacious rooms with volume ceilings and grand arches define interior living areas. This exciting show home features interesting shapes and angles. Each room holds the viewer's attention with its unique use of space and architectural details.

To the right of the entry is the formal dining room. This area has a detailed step ceiling and is open to a built-in serving bar off the gallery. Corner pocket sliding glass doors in the living room bring the outdoor views inside. Through a groin vault vestibule, you pass the wet bar to the family areas.

Stone columns flank the entrance and give the feeling of openness by replacing walls to define living and dining room areas.

The formal dining room's limestone floor with marble inlay complements graceful arches and sculpted columns.

63

The home's fully equipped kitchen is as lovely as it is functional. Designed with cen[tral] island and walk-in pantry, it overlooks the nearby family room and breakfast nook.

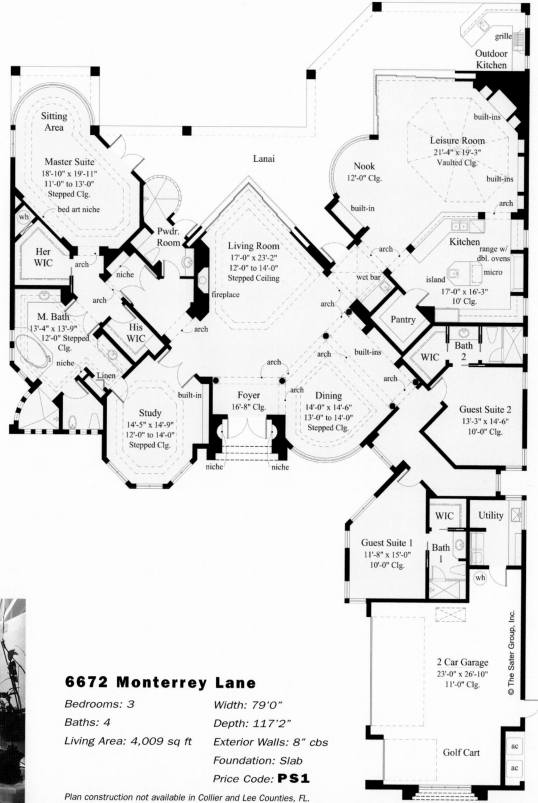

The master retreat features a detailed stone bedroom wall and cozy sitting area with outside pool and patio views. The pampering bath features a relaxing garden tub and his and her vanities. Natural light is provided by the detailed privacy window, which again features the "diagonal cross" design element.

6672 Monterrey Lane

Bedrooms: 3

Baths: 4

Living Area: 4,009 sq ft

Width: 79'0"

Depth: 117'2"

Exterior Walls: 8" cbs

Foundation: Slab

Price Code: **PS1**

Plan construction not available in Collier and Lee Counties, FL.

milano

This spectacular home was designed to take full advantage of its waterfront location. Glass walls expand interior spaces and grant full view of nature's splendor.

With glamorous curves and varied angles, the Milano is certain to match the views wherever it is built. Grand, stately columns and cast stone balusters line the plan's masterful design, accenting its breathtaking views.

Tailored amenities include a master foyer, a master garden with water feature, a plush master bath suite containing a morning kitchen, an exercise room and pool bath. Other features include an octagonal study, a deluxe guest suite, a circular breakfast nook, a library/loft, a media room, an observation deck, an outdoor kitchen, a barrel-vaulted porte-cochere, a built-in fireplace and more. Corner pocket sliding glass doors in the wide, open living room provide a vantage point to the home's interior and exterior views.

Whether by day or night,
enjoy the dramatic vistas
from any of the living areas.
Views are central to this
home's architecture.

The kitchen looks beyond the breakfast nook and leisure room to exquisite views. The resident chef will appreciate built-in appliances and ample storage.

Images become life size in your state-of-the-art media room.

Fixed and moving walls of glass offer exquisite views beyond. Pools of water define living areas, and create an open and airy feeling.

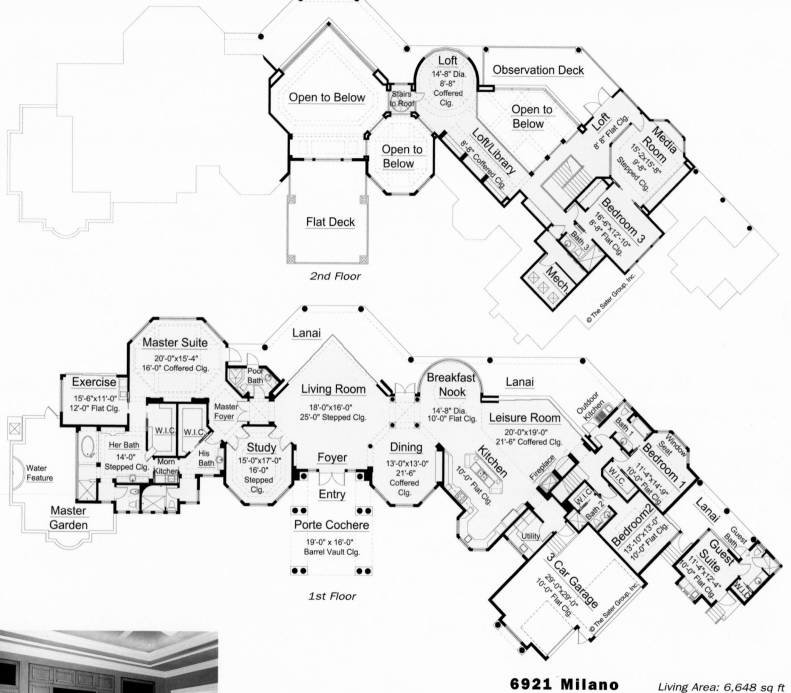

Loft
14'-8" Dia.
8'-8"
Coffered
Clg.

Observation Deck

Open to Below

Stairs to Roof

Open to Below

Open to Below

Loft/Library
8'-8" Coffered Clg.

Loft
8'-8" Flat Clg.

Media Room
15'-2"x15'-8"
9'-8"
Stepped Clg.

Bedroom 3
16'-6"x12'-10"
8'-8" Flat Clg.

Bath 3

Mech.

Flat Deck

© The Sater Group, Inc.

2nd Floor

Master Suite
20'-0"x15'-4"
16'-0" Coffered Clg.

Lanai

Exercise
15'-6"x11'-0"
12'-0" Flat Clg.

Pool Bath

Living Room
18'-0"x16'-0"
25'-0" Stepped Clg.

Breakfast Nook
14'-8" Dia.
10'-0" Flat Clg.

Lanai

Leisure Room
20'-0"x19'-0"
21'-6" Coffered Clg.

Outdoor Kitchen

Master Foyer

W.I.C.

W.I.C.

Her Bath
14'-0"
Stepped Clg.

Morn Kitchen

His Bath

Study
15'-0"x17'-0"
16'-0" Stepped Clg.

Foyer

Dining
13'-0"x13'-0"
21'-6" Coffered Clg.

Kitchen
10'-0" Flat Clg.

Fireplace

Bath 1

Bedroom 1
11'-4"x14'-9"
10'-0" Flat Clg.

Window Seat

Water Feature

Entry

W.I.C.

Bath 2

W.I.C.

Lanai

Guest Bath

Master Garden

Porte Cochere
19'-0" x 16'-0"
Barrel Vault Clg.

Utility

Bedroom 2
13'-10"x13'-0"
10'-0" Flat Clg.

Guest Suite
11'-4"x12'-4"
10'-0" Flat Clg.

W.I.C.

3 Car Garage
29'-0"x29'-0"
10'-0" Flat Clg.

© The Sater Group, Inc.

1st Floor

6921 Milano

Bedrooms: 5

Baths: 7

1st Floor: 4,842 sq ft

2nd Floor: 1,524 sq ft

Guest Suite: 282 sq ft

Living Area: 6,648 sq ft

Width: 174'10"

Depth: 81'2"

Exterior Walls: 8" cbs

Foundation: Slab

Price Code: **PSE8**

Plan construction not available in Collier and Lee Counties, FL.

broadmoor walk

The grand foyer opens to a combined living room and dining room, created especially for entertaining with a wet bar, fireplace and access to the lanai through a trio of French doors. The home's less formal family areas are located to the right of the plan — the kitchen, nook and leisure room, where a free flow of space and windows focus on sweeping views to the rear of the home.

The curves and lines of the free-flowing pool add drama to the home's large outdoor area, which is embraced by the leisure room, to the right of the plan, and the master suite and its sitting area to the left. A covered lanai, situated conveniently off of the leisure room, has an outdoor kitchen and a powder bathroom, perfect for entertaining under the stars.

In addition to welcoming in an abundance of sunshine, windows on the front facade allow for intimate views of the front gardens from the study and one of two guest rooms. Windows take on an interesting assortment of shapes — from squares and rectangles to a sunburst window above the elegant entry door and the circle of glass inside the door. Round columns and quoin detailing make an elegant statement on the home's exterior.

The family areas of the home are marked by a free flow of space between the island kitchen, nook and leisure room. Counter seating offers the only recognition of boundaries between these rooms, which are situated to enjoy views of the lanai and backyard. The cook of the home will enjoy an abundance of counter and cabinet space, including a walk-in pantry.

The master suite has his-and-her walk-in closets and built-ins flanking the entrance to the bathroom, which features double sinks, a step-up oval tub, and round glass block shower that welcomes in light but maintains privacy.

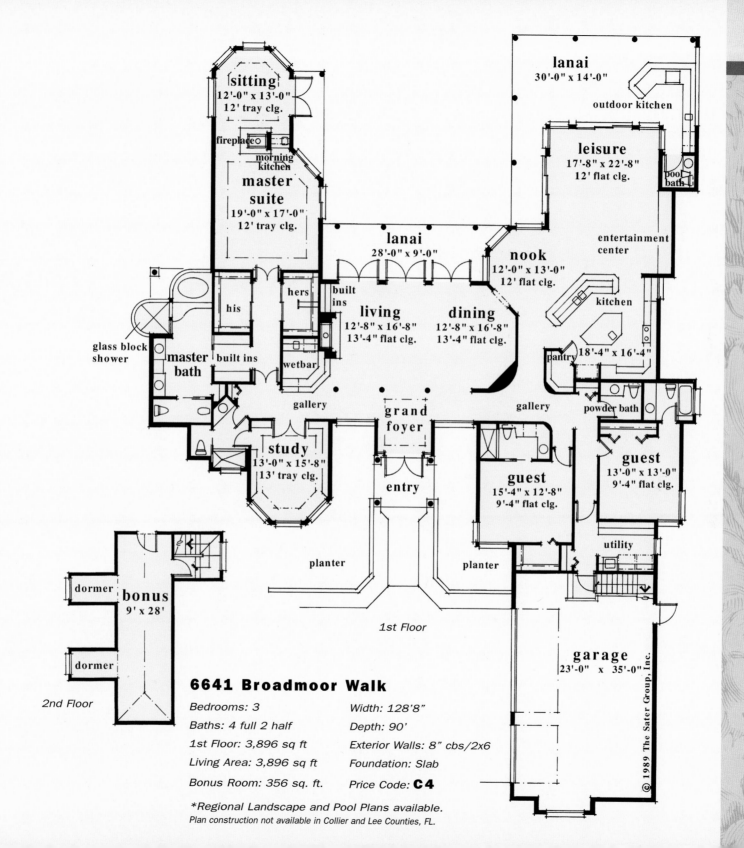

sitting
12'-0" x 13'-0"
12' tray clg.

fireplace

morning kitchen

master suite
19'-0" x 17'-0"
12' tray clg.

lanai
30'-0" x 14'-0"

outdoor kitchen

leisure
17'-8" x 22'-8"
12' flat clg.

pool bath

entertainment center

his

hers

built ins

lanai
28'-0" x 9'-0"

nook
12'-0" x 13'-0"
12' flat clg.

kitchen
18'-4" x 16'-4"

glass block shower

master bath

built ins

wetbar

living
12'-8" x 16'-8"
13'-4" flat clg.

dining
12'-8" x 16'-8"
13'-4" flat clg.

pantry

gallery

grand foyer

gallery

powder bath

study
13'-0" x 15'-8"
13' tray clg.

entry

guest
15'-4" x 12'-8"
9'-4" flat clg.

guest
13'-0" x 13'-0"
9'-4" flat clg.

planter

planter

utility

1st Floor

dormer

bonus
9' x 28'

dormer

2nd Floor

garage
23'-0" x 35'-0"

© 1989 The Sater Group, Inc.

6641 Broadmoor Walk

Bedrooms: 3

Baths: 4 full 2 half

1st Floor: 3,896 sq ft

Living Area: 3,896 sq ft

Bonus Room: 356 sq. ft.

Width: 128'8"

Depth: 90'

Exterior Walls: 8" cbs/2x6

Foundation: Slab

Price Code: **C4**

*Regional Landscape and Pool Plans available.

Plan construction not available in Collier and Lee Counties, FL.

turnberry lane

Classic columns, circle-head windows and a bow window study give this stucco home a wonderful street presence. The double arched entryway provides balanced elegance. Inside the foyer, a mitered glass window provides an open feel while viewing a garden to the left of the entry. The formal living and dining rooms are straight ahead providing one with a captivating first impression of elegance. An arched buffet server separates those rooms while providing an open feeling.

Mitered glass and French doors allow for rear yard views and natural light.

This plan comes with options for a front car garage for different lot situations.

Walk through the gallery toward the family areas and the truly convenient part of this home comes to life. An ample kitchen has a walk-in pantry, center prep island sink, an eating bar and desk space. The open nook is conveniently located for the family eating times.

The leisure room, shown on next page, provides a peaceful retreat focusing on a fireplace and built-in entertainment center space while adding to the home's custom feel.

The master wing hosts a convenient study and ample sleeping area, as well as his and her wardrobe closets and an alluring bath. A private water closet room has built-ins perfect for linens. A walk-in shower and garden tub focuses out to an optional private garden that makes this home truly sumptuous.

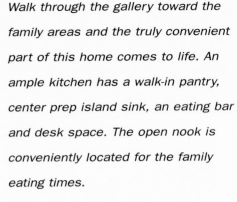

guest 1
14'-8" x 11'-10"
10' flat clg.

outdoor kitchen

verandah
38'-0" x 15'-0"

master suite
14'-8" x 16'-0"
11' flat clg.

leisure
19'-0" x 17'-0"
10' flat clg.

mitered glass

WIC

private garden

fireplace

nook
9'-0" x 11'-0"

dining
12'-0" x 15'-0"
12' flat clg.

living
15'-0" x 16'-0"
14' tray clg.

master foyer

kitchen

buffet server

WIC

15' x 14' pantry

gallery

make-up

master bath

utility

mitered glass

foyer

guest 2
11'-0" x 13'-2"
10' flat clg.

garden

study
11'-8" x 14'-0"
12' flat clg.

mitered glass

entry

© The Sater Group, Inc.

garage
23'-0" x 37'-6"

6602 Turnberry Lane

Bedrooms: 3

Baths: 3

Living Area: 2,794 sq ft

Width: 70'

Depth: 98'

Exterior Walls: 2x6/8" cbs

Foundation: Slab

Price Code: **C2**

77

Plan construction not available in Collier and Lee Counties, FL.

wentworth trail

The elegance of brick and stucco create a classic, traditional ambience for this two-story home. Designed for entertaining on a grand scale or just relaxing and enjoying life's slower pace, the home is readily accommodating. Large, open areas can just as easily play host to a large formal party as they can to a quiet night at home with the family.

The foyer opens directly onto the home's formal spaces — the living room straight ahead and the dining room to the right of the plan. Space between the two flows freely and can be expanded to the rear lanai and backyard views by opening zero-corner sliding glass doors in the living room. The high stepped ceiling in the living room provides a grand feel.

The plan is created to showcase the perfect setting — a golf course lot, waterfront property or wooded acreage. Floor-to-ceiling windows dominate most of the rooms facing the covered lanai, affording the opportunity for sweeping, unending views.

A stepped ceiling in the dining room soars high, while windows offer a colorful view of the front garden spot.

Archways extend a comfortable welcome to the plan's family spaces — the kitchen, nook, leisure room, and guest rooms. The gourmet kitchen has a walk-in pantry, cooktop island and an eating bar.

The master wing benefits from a private retreat to the left of the plan. The bedroom overlooks backyard views through a bayed area and through triple sliding glass doors that lead to a private area of the lanai. A garden tub gazes over a private garden space — a view that can also be enjoyed from the glass shower or experienced in person by a door that leads to this private oasis. The bathroom also has his-and-her vanity areas and a large walk-in closet.

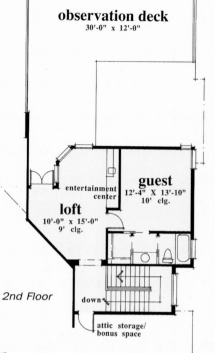

observation deck
30'-0" x 12'-0"

guest
12'-4" X 13'-10"
10' clg.

entertainment
center

loft
10'-0" x 15'-0"
9' clg.

2nd Floor

down

attic storage/
bonus space

lanai
30'-0" x 10'-0"

outdoor
kitchen

leisure
15'-10" x 18'-0"
stepped clg.

fireplace

dry
bar

lanai
31'-0" x 10'-0"

nook
8' x 10'
10' clg.

kitchen

master
17'-0" x 14'-9"
13'-4" tray clg.

living
15'-0" x 15'-0"
14'-4" clg.

arch

pantry 12' x 14'

arch

w.i.c.

arch

arch

arch

up

arch

stor.

books

mir.

study
10' x 11'
13'-4" clg.

foyer

dining
11'-0" x 14'-0"
15'-0" tray clg.

arch

his hers

entry

planter

**master
bath**

glass
shwr.

planter

planter

util.

guest
12'-0" x 11'-0"
10' clg.

master garden

planter

storage

1st Floor

garage
21'-0" x 28'-6"

© The Sater Group, Inc.

6653 Wenthworth Trail

Bedrooms: 3	Width: 67'
Baths: 3-1/2	Depth: 102'
1st Floor: 2,894 sq ft	Exterior Walls: 8" cbs
2nd Floor: 568 sq ft	Foundation: slab
Living Area: 3,462 sq ft	Price Code: **C3**

Plan construction not available in Collier and Lee Counties, FL.

81

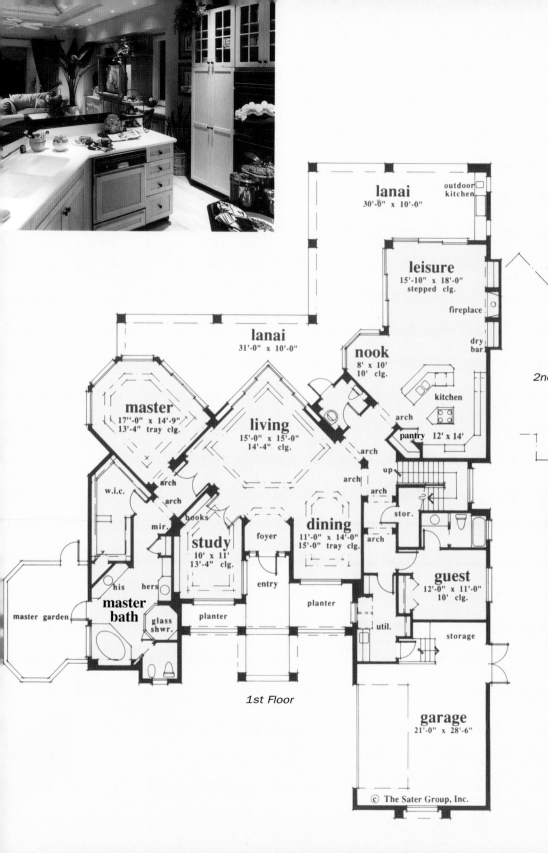

biltmore trace

A clean, but wonderfully exciting exterior only hints at the unique floor plan that waits. Curved bay windows in the dining room and study give the facade of this stucco home a gracious custom design look. Columns add architectural interest as does banding around windows and rooflines. Undulating walls and the L-shaped flow of the home create eye-pleasing variations of light and shadow. A raised entryway with double doors leads into a foyer, where a glass wall overlooks a fountain and atrium.

A formal living room and dining room are located to the left of the main gallery hallway. The dining room enjoys a garden spot overlooking front garden areas, while the intimate living room overlooks both the fountain and atrium and the covered lanai. Arches and a raised ceiling define the formal spaces.

Zero-corner sliding glass doors pocket into the wall to open the leisure room to the covered lanai.

The master bathroom has a large walk-in closet, a glass shower, a soaking tub overlooking a private garden area, and dual vanities.

The kitchen, nook and leisure room are designed for enjoyable family living and casual entertaining.

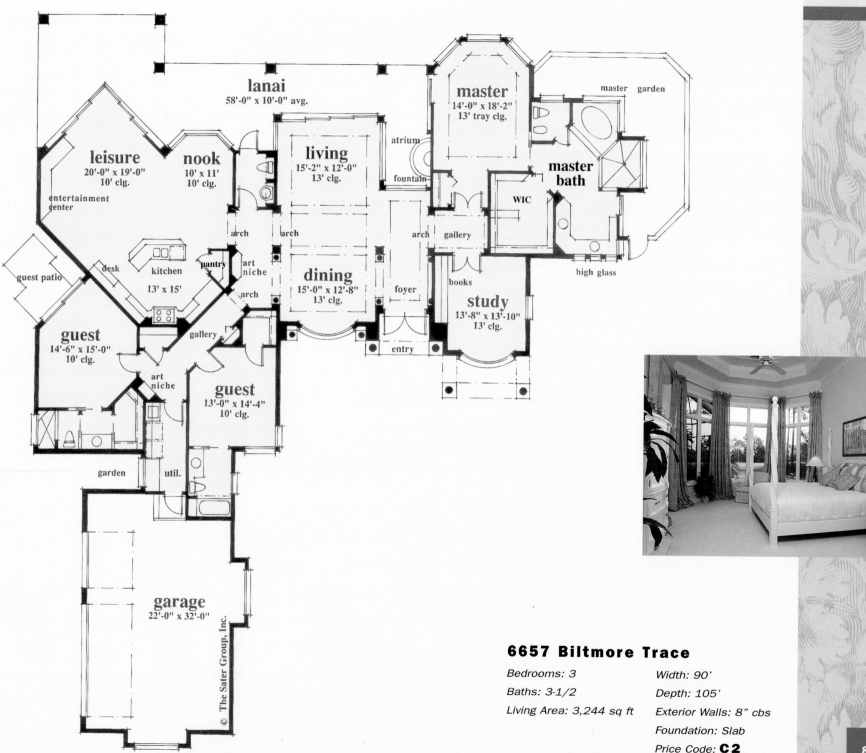

lanai
58'-0" x 10'-0" avg.

master
14'-0" x 18'-2"
13' tray clg.

master garden

leisure
20'-0" x 19'-0"
10' clg.

nook
10' x 11'
10' clg.

living
15'-2" x 12'-0"
13' clg.

atrium

master
bath

entertainment
center

fountain

WIC

guest patio

desk

kitchen
13' x 15'

pantry

art
niche

arch

arch

arch

gallery

arch

dining
15'-0" x 12'-8"
13' clg.

books

high glass

guest
14'-6" x 15'-0"
10' clg.

gallery

art
niche

foyer

study
13'-8" x 13'-10"
13' clg.

art
niche

guest
13'-0" x 14'-4"
10' clg.

entry

garden

util.

© The Sater Group, Inc.

garage
22'-0" x 32'-0"

6657 Biltmore Trace

Bedrooms: 3

Baths: 3-1/2

Living Area: 3,244 sq ft

Width: 90'

Depth: 105'

Exterior Walls: 8" cbs

Foundation: Slab

Price Code: **C2**

Plan construction not available in Collier and Lee Counties, FL.

LIGHTING

LiteTouch automatically controls lights, security, thermostat and more when you awake, return home, entertain – anything you want, any time you want.

CONTROL MAKES EVERY HOME A DREAM HOME.

A LiteTouch lighting control system does so much more than just turn lights on and off – it enriches your life by making your new home more efficient, comfortable and secure.

With just the touch of a button, LiteTouch lets you automatically create the perfect lighting for every room, time of day and mood. What's more, LiteTouch provides total home automation control by integrating with drapes, audio/video equipment, appliances and anything else in your home that runs on electricity.

For more information about LiteTouch, contact your architect, lighting designer or call us at **1-888-LITETCH (548-3824)**.

Whether you're in the mood for a lively party or a relaxing dinner, LiteTouch allows you to create just the right atmosphere for dining or entertaining.

LiteTouch helps make your home theatre even better by integrating lighting, audio/video equipment, drapes, projection screens and more.

LiteTouch control stations are available in a wide range of styles, colors and finishes to compliment the décor of your new home. Custom engraving allows you to personalize the buttons on each control station.

LiteTouch®
Brilliant Solutions in Lighting Automation

Royal Palm

Triple arches — in the entryway and windows to the right of the plan — create a commanding presence for this two-story home and its dominantly hipped rooflines. Elegant columns, traditional stucco and stone detailing reflect Mediterranean influences.

© The Sater Group

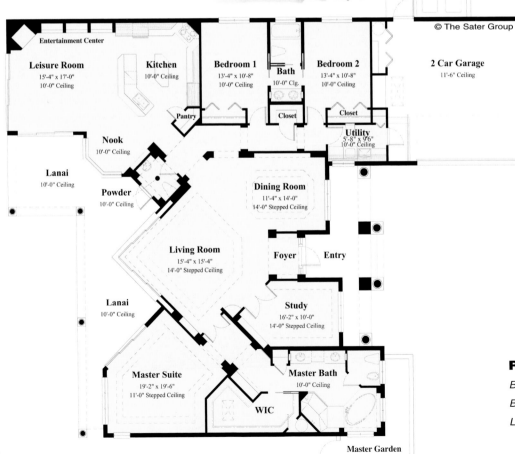

© The Sater Group

Entertainment Center

Leisure Room
15'-4" x 17'-0"
10'-0" Ceiling

Kitchen
10'-0" Ceiling

Bedroom 1
13'-4" x 10'-8"
10'-0" Ceiling

Bath
10'-0" Clg.

Bedroom 2
13'-4" x 10'-8"
10'-0" Ceiling

2 Car Garage
11'-6" Ceiling

Pantry

Closet

Closet

Utility
5'-8" x 9'6"
10'-0" Ceiling

Nook
10'-0" Ceiling

Lanai
10'-0" Ceiling

Powder
10'-0" Ceiling

Dining Room
11'-4" x 14'-0"
14'-0" Stepped Ceiling

Living Room
15'-4" x 15'-4"
14'-0" Stepped Ceiling

Foyer

Entry

Lanai
10'-0" Ceiling

Study
16'-2" x 10'-0"
14'-0" Stepped Ceiling

Master Suite
19'-2" x 19'-6"
11'-0" Stepped Ceiling

Master Bath
10'-0" Ceiling

WIC

Master Garden

Plan 6727

Bedrooms: 3

Baths: 2-1/2

Living Area: 2,823 sq ft

Width: 65'

Depth: 84'4"

Exterior Walls: 8" cbs

Foundation: Slab

Price Code: **C3**

Coral Harbor

Quoined corners, a trio of sunburst windows, dramatic roof overhangs and shutters grace the front of this elegant home. An undulating roof furthers the visual impact.

© The Sater Group

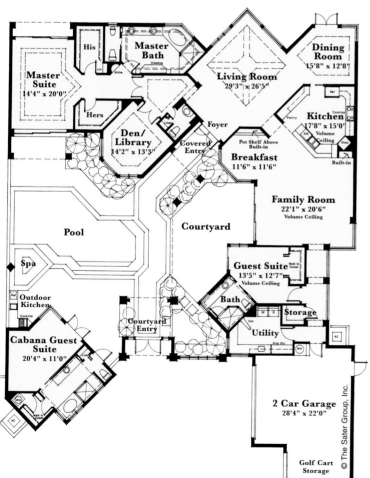

© The Sater Group, Inc.

Landscaping extends a warm welcome to guests entering this home through a private courtyard — a feature borrowed from the villas of the Mediterranean. Guests are led to the covered entry by a walkway, past a large courtyard and a space that is an ideal location for a pool and spa.

Plan 6728

Bedrooms: 3 + 1 Guest

Baths: 3-1/2 + 1 Guest

Guest Suite: 438 sq ft

Living Area: 3,696 sq ft

Width: 80'

Depth: 107'3"

Exterior Walls: 8" cbs

Foundation: Slab

Price Code: **L1**

Hillcrest Ridge

This grand traditional home offers a wonderful blend of open and formal spaces in a design that feels much larger than it really is. From the street, the brick triple arched entryway warmly welcomes you into the home.

© The Sater Group

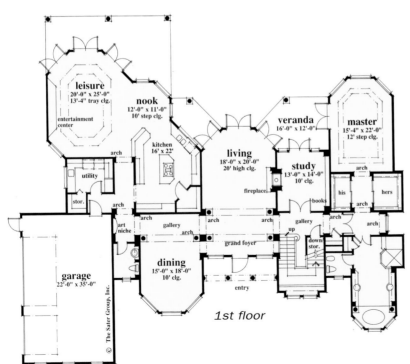

1st floor

- leisure 20'-0" x 25'-0" 13'-4" tray clg.
- entertainment center
- nook 12'-0" x 11'-0" 10' step clg.
- kitchen 16' x 22'
- utility
- stor.
- art niche
- garage 22'-0" x 35'-0"
- dining 15'-0" x 18'-0" 10' clg.
- living 18'-0" x 20'-0" 20' high clg.
- fireplace
- veranda 16'-0" x 12'-0"
- study 13'-4" x 14'-0" 10' clg.
- books
- his
- hers
- master 15'-4" x 22'-0" 12' step clg.
- gallery
- grand foyer
- up
- down stor.
- entry
- arch

© The Sater Group, Inc.

2nd floor

- balcony
- balcony
- br. 2 15'-0" x 15'-8" 9' clg.
- open to living room below
- br. 3 13'-6" x 14'-6" 9' clg.
- br. 4 15'-0" x 16'-0" 9' clg.
- open to foyer below
- arch
- down

© The Sater Group, Inc.

*Regional Landscape and Pool Plans available.

Plan 6651

Bedrooms: 4
Baths: 3-1/2
1st Floor: 3,546 sq ft
2nd Floor: 1,213 sq ft
Living Area: 4,759 sq ft

Width: 95'4"
Depth: 83'
Exterior Walls: 2x6
Foundation: Slab or basement
Price Code: **L2**

Cotton Creek

This grand plan is truly a perfect representation of traditional elegance with an updated contemporary feel. Inside the grand foyer, the plan opens up to the formal living spaces through archways. The high stepped ceilings open the rooms and give it a grand airy feel.

© The Sater Group

1st floor

2nd floor

Plan 6650

Bedrooms: 4

Baths: 4

1st Floor: 3,092 sq ft

2nd Floor: 656 sq ft

Living Area: 3,748 sq ft

Width: 77'4"

Depth: 93'10"

Exterior Walls: 8" cbs

Foundation: Slab

Price Code: **C3**

Elk River Lane

An elegant blend of exterior materials makes this home a visual beauty. A raised study, barrel vault entryway and a two-story turret make this home look and feel larger than it really is. The open and free-flowing plan is perfect for families, empty nesters or move-up homebuyers. The design also comes with an optional basement layout.

© The Sater Group

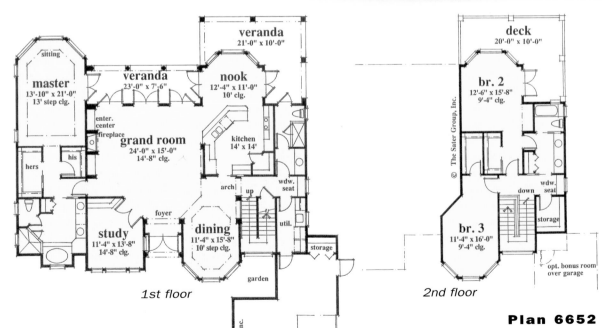

1st floor

2nd floor

*Regional Landscape and Pool Plans available.

Plan 6652

Bedrooms: 3
Baths: 3
1st Floor: 2,181 sq ft
2nd Floor: 710 sq ft
Living Area: 2,891 sq ft

Width: 66'4"
Depth: 79'
Exterior Walls: 2x6
Foundation: Slab or basement
Price Code: **C2**

Stoney Creek Way

This grand plan is truly a perfect representation of traditional elegance with an updated contemporary feel. The look is graceful and commanding with plenty of curbside appeal. The high stepped ceilings open the rooms and give it a grand airy feel.

© The Sater Group

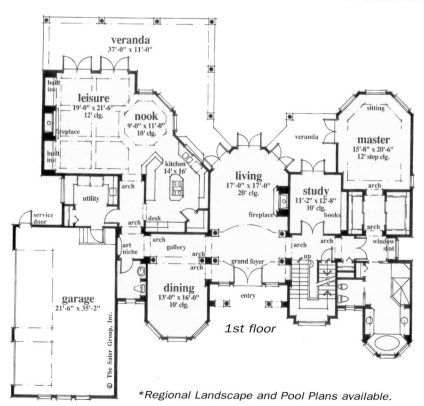

veranda
37'-0" x 11'-0"

leisure
19'-0" x 21'-6"
12' clg.

nook
9'-0" x 11'-0"
10' clg.

built ins
fireplace
built ins

kitchen
14' x 16'

utility

service door

arch

garage
21'-6" x 35'-2"

© The Sater Group, Inc.

art niche

desk

arch

arch

gallery

arch

arch

dining
13'-0" x 16'-0"
10' clg.

living
17'-0" x 17'-0"
20' clg.

fireplace

grand foyer

entry

up

study
11'-2" x 12'-8"
10' clg.

books

veranda

master
15'-8" x 20'-6"
12' step clg.

sitting

arch

arch

window seat

1st floor

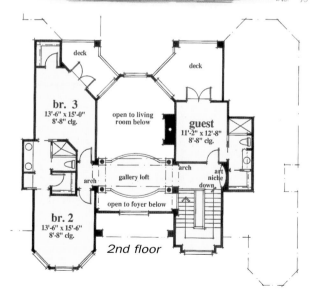

deck

deck

br. 3
13'-6" x 15'-0"
8'-8" clg.

open to living room below

guest
11'-2" x 12'-8"
8'-8" clg.

art niche

gallery loft

arch

down

open to foyer below

br. 2
13'-6" x 15'-6"
8'-8" clg.

2nd floor

Regional Landscape and Pool Plans available.

Plan 6656

Bedrooms: 4

Baths: 3-1/2

1st Floor: 3,027 sq ft

2nd Floor: 1,079 sq ft

Living Area: 4,106 sq ft

Width: 87'4"

Depth: 80'4"

Exterior Walls: 2x6

Foundation: Slab or basement

Price Code: **L1**

Queenstown Harbor

This wonderfully balanced exterior has triple columns at the covered entry porch. Circle-top windows add a custom look and are carried throughout the exterior. Graceful rooflines give the home grand presence. The master suite has a bayed area looking out to the rear views and is perfect for chairs or a couch for a relaxing sitting retreat. The bath has a large soaking tub viewing the private garden, dual vanities, a large shower and his and her walk-in closets.

© The Sater Group

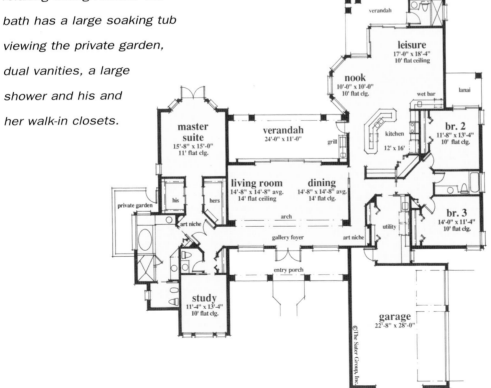

The leisure room has an optional wet bar area and glass doors that open to another covered verandah. An outdoor bath is off the verandah and can be used as a mud bath or pool cabana.

Plan 6663

Bedrooms: 3
Baths: 3-1/2
Living Area: 2,978 sq ft

Width: 84'
Depth: 90'
Exterior Walls: 8" cbs
Foundation: Slab
Price Code: **C2**

*Regional Landscape and Pool Plans available.

Fiddler's Creek

As you enter the grand foyer, the two-story living room features bay glass windows and custom doors. A double-sided fireplace is shared with the study. Across from the study, a glass turret surrounds the spiral staircase. High ceilings, oversized rooms and an elegant facade make this home a timeless choice.

© The Sater Group

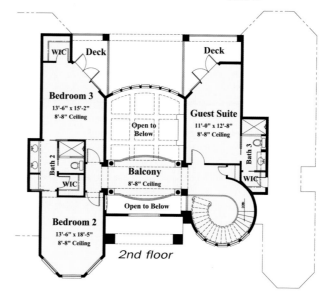

Plan 6746

Bedrooms: 4

Baths: 3-1/2

1st Floor: 2,841 sq ft

2nd Floor: 1,052 sq ft

Living Area: 3,893 sq ft

Width: 85'

Depth: 76'2"

Exterior Walls: 2x6

Foundation: Basement

Price Code: **L1**

Plantation Pine

This old world style Italianate home only hints at the unique floor plan that awaits. The formal living and dining room have triple French doors that allow for easy outdoor living. This home provides plenty of living space with an elegant exterior. Focused around the outdoors, the main living areas have windows or doors taking advantage of the natural surroundings.

HOLZHAUER INC.

© The Sater Group

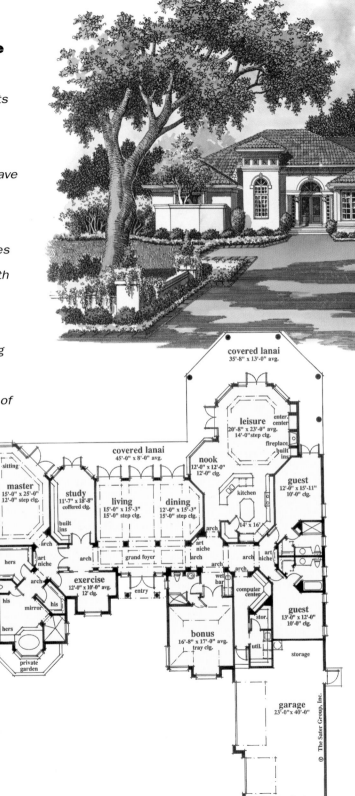

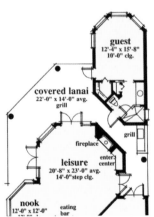

Guest Suite Option

Plan 6735

Bedrooms: 4

Baths: 5

Living Area: 4,282 sq ft

Guest Suite: 333 sq ft

Width: 119'

Depth: 88'

Exterior Walls: 2x6

Foundation: Slab

Price Code: **C4**

Innsbrook Place

An angled garage, raised entry and turret study help create a visually exciting and different streetscape. The angled theme is present throughout the design and is useful in view orientation.
The master has a spacious suite. The area has a warming fireplace, a morning kitchen bar, and lanai access.

© The Sater Group

built ins
fireplace

leisure
23'-0" x 17'-8"
12'-6" flat clg.

lanai

nook
10'-8" x 10'-8"
12' step clg.

lanai
30'-0" x 10'-0"

grill

kitchen

bedroom
13'-4" x 13'-8"
9'-4" flat clg.

wetbar

master suite
17'-0" x 20'-4"
14' flat clg.

living
15'-0" x 17'-2"
14' flat clg.

gallery

am kitchen

2 view firplace

his

hers

dining
17'-0" x 13'-0"
14' flat clg.

utility

foyer

gallery

entry

planter

bedroom
13'-4" x 12'-0"
9'-4" flat clg.

study
13'-0" x 15'-8"
14' vault clg.

© 1990 The Sater Group, Inc.

garage
23'-4" x 29'-8"

Pass through the archway and you enter the informal family area. An octagon nook has windows open to all rear views. The leisure room has optional fixed glass windows above the entertainment center and a gas fireplace that allows for natural light and a visually exciting detail.

Plan 6634

Bedrooms: 3
Baths: 3-1/2
Living Area: 3,477 sq ft

Width: 95'
Depth: 88'8"
Exterior Walls: 8" cbs
Foundation: Slab
Price Code: **C3**

Spring Hill Lane

A wonderful streetscape is pronounced on this family stucco home. A turret study and raised entry highlight this elegant residence. Half-round columns at the entry add an elegant look, while giving the design a custom feel so it blends into any neighborhood. Inside the home, columns frame the living room ahead. Glass doors open to the veranda and rear views beyond. The entire home is focused around the outdoors. All the main living spaces have glass windows or doors to the outside to take advantage of natural light and ventilation.

© The Sater Group

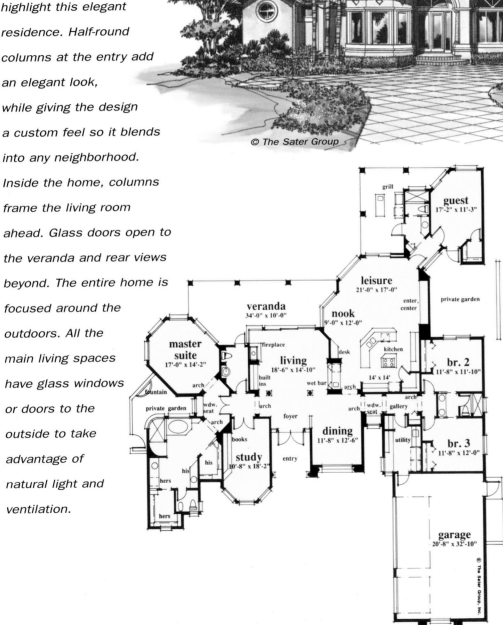

Plan 6661

Bedrooms: 4

Baths: 3-1/2

Living Area: 3,265 sq ft

Width: 80'

Depth: 103'8"

Exterior Walls: 8" cbs

Foundation: Slab

Price Code: **C3**

*Regional Landscape and Pool Plans available.

Governors Club

This custom feel ranch-style home provides a sprawling layout that opens the living spaces to the rear yard views. The porte cochere gives the owners and guests covered parking that leads to double entry doors opening to the grand foyer. The formal living room is straight ahead and offers expansive back yard views through a mitered glass wall. A high-coffered ceiling adds to the open feel of the home.

© The Sater Group

The rear-load garage provides optimum privacy. The garage placement on an angle also creates the true estate ranch feel.

Plan 6674

Bedrooms: 3
Baths: 3-1/2
Living Area: 3,398 sq ft

Width: 121'5"
Depth: 96'2"
Exterior Walls: 8" cbs
Foundation: Slab
Price Code: **C2**

Annapolis Trail
Lyman Orchard

The facade is clean and elegant with a mix of brick and stucco and high-pitched rooflines. Inside, the living room opens to a covered lanai facing the rear yard through pocket sliding glass doors. The open kitchen, nook and leisure room all focus towards the built-in entertainment center and the outdoor views.

This clean and simplified design blends a livable layout with a traditional exterior that makes this a great home for any region.

HOLZHAUER INC. © The Sater Group   6720 Annapolis Trail

© The Sater Group   6726 Lyman Orchard

© The Sater Group, Inc.

Floor plan labels:
enter. center
study 11'-0" x 13'-0" 10'-0" clg.
leisure 15'-6" X 18'-6" 11'-0" step clg.
nook 8'-0" X 10'-0" 10'-0" clg.
butt joint glass
covered lanai 28'-2" x 9'-6"
desk
br. 2 11'-0" x 11'-4" 10'-0" clg.
eating bar
kitchen
13' x 15'
pant.
living 17'-6" x 15'-0" avg. 12'-0" clg.
master 14'-0" x 17'-2" 12'-0" tray clg.
arch
gallery
arch
arch
arch
br. 3 13'-4" x 11'-8" 10'-0" clg.
util.
dining 12'-3" x 12'-0" 12'-0" clg.
arch
his
w.i.c.
stor.
hers
dress.
covered entry
garage 20'-8" x 25'-0"

Plan 6720/6726

Bedrooms: 3
Baths: 3
Living Area: 2,723 sq ft

Width: 62'
Depth: 80'4"
Exterior Walls: 8" cbs/2
Foundation: Slab
Price Code: **C1**

Timber Point
Inwood Forest

The traditional exterior and raised entry with clean detailing give this home great curb appeal. The dining room is highlighted with arches and columns while the living room faces the rear view. The kitchen is open with plenty of counter and storage space. Some of the extras include a large pantry and a prep island for extra workspace.

In the leisure room a built-in entertainment center has high glass above to allow light to fill the room.

© The Sater Group

6717 Timber Point

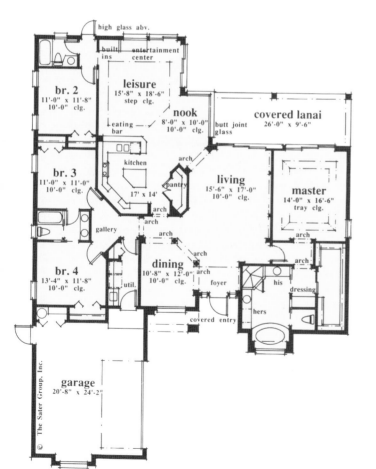

© The Sater Group

6718 Inwood Forest

Plan 6717/6718

Bedrooms: 4

Baths: 3

Living Area: 2,508 sq ft

Width: 78'9"

Depth: 60'

Exterior Walls: 8" cbs

Foundation: Slab

Price Code: **C1**

East Lake Way
Cypress Bay

This interesting home features a raised entry, detailed columns, and a stucco or stucco and brick mixed exterior. Large glass windows and doors allow natural light and the outdoors inside.

The master suite opens to the lanai through glass doors and features many amenities including a master bath with a luxurious tub that looks out to the garden area beyond.

© The Sater Group

6711 East Lake Way

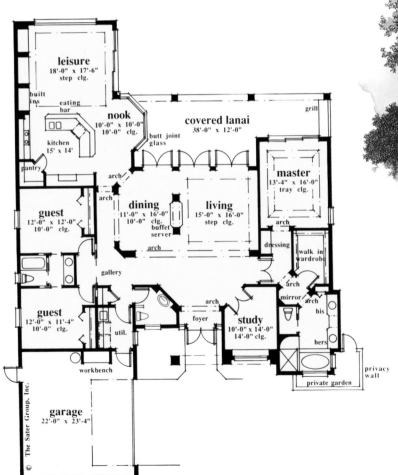

© The Sater Group

6714 Cypress Ba

Plan 6711/6714

Bedrooms: 3

Baths: 2-1/2

Living Area: 2,856 sq ft

Width: 63'4"

Depth: 87

Exterior Walls: 2x6

Foundation: Slab

Price Code: **C3**

Cedar Brook Court
Landfall Trail

This special home uniquely blends brick and stucco to give it a southern traditional feel. Inside the home, the open floor plan allows the formal spaces to feel grand while allowing the outdoors in.

Corner pocket sliding glass doors at the living room open completely and let the lanai become part of the home.

© The Sater Group

6710 Cedar Brook Court

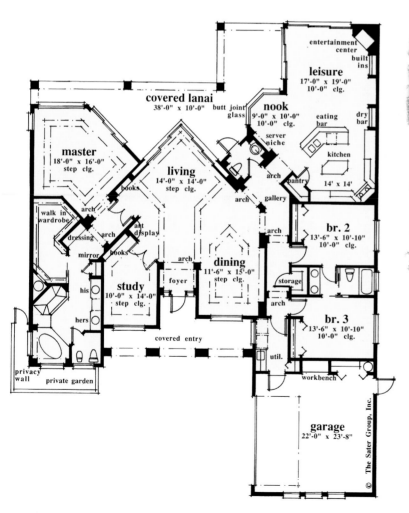

© The Sater Group, Inc.

© The Sater Group

6719 Landfall Trail

Plan 6710/6719

Bedrooms: 3

Baths: 2-1/2

Living Area: 2,907 sq ft

Width: 65'

Depth: 84'

Exterior Walls: 2x6

Foundation: Slab

Price Code: **C3**

Griffith Parkway
Reynolds Plantation

The unique exterior of this home has a high-pitched roof with dormer detailing and brick and stucco to give it a southern traditional feel. A raised entry uses large columns to give the area a warm welcome. The living room has corner sliding glass doors to the covered lanai.

Step ceiling detailing in the formal living and dining rooms adds a custom touch. Arches and columns lead you toward the family area. In the relaxing area, an open kitchen, nook and leisure room highlight the space.

© The Sater Group

6721 Griffith Parkway

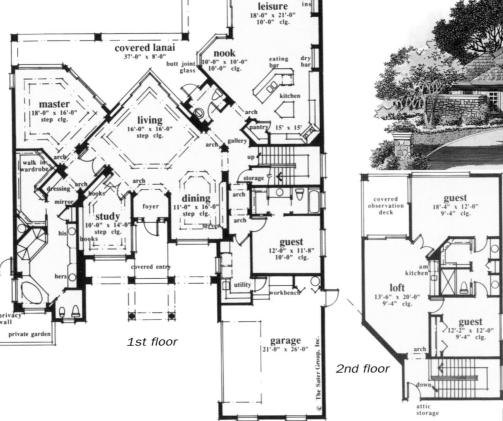

1st floor

2nd floor

© The Sater Group   *6722 Reynolds Plantation*

Plan 6721/6722

Bedrooms: 4	Width: 65'
Baths: 3-1/2	Depth: 91'
1st Floor: 3,010 sq ft	Exterior Walls: 2x6
2nd Floor: 948 sq ft	Foundation: Slab
Living Area: 3,958 sq ft	Price Code: **L1**

Willow Bend
Jupiter Hills

An arched entryway provides a warm welcome. A clear blend of brick and stucco give this residence a traditional feel. Inside the foyer, the formal dining room is to the left and highlighted by arched columns. Ahead, the formal living has glass doors to the covered lanai at the rear. The kitchen, nook and leisure room are open for a comfortable retreat for the family. The master suite has a tray ceiling and glass doors to the covered lanai.

© The Sater Group

6712 Willow Bend

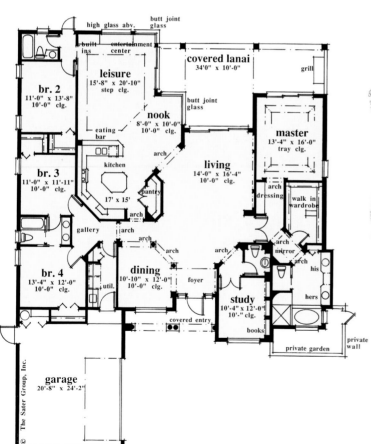

© The Sater Group

6713 Jupiter Hills

Plan 6712/6713

Bedrooms: 4

Baths: 3-1/2

Living Area: 3,036 sq ft

Width: 63'10"

Depth: 84'

Exterior Walls: 2x6/8" cbs

Foundation: Slab

Price Code: **C4**

Bellaire Lane
Sanctuary Court

A raised double-arched entryway, high-pitched roof, columned study and dormers give this home great street presence. The brick and stucco exterior create a warm and elegant feel. Archways and art spaces give the gallery halls a custom touch. The master suite has a bayed sitting area, a step ceiling and French doors to the covered lanai, and many extra amenities in the master bath to pamper the owners.

© The Sater Group   6715 Bellaire Lane

© The Sater Group   6716 Sanctuary Court

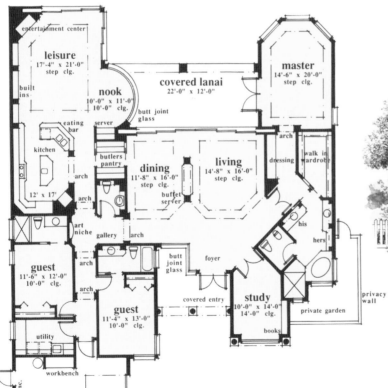

Plan 6715/6716

Bedrooms: 3

Baths: 3-1/2

Living Area 3,185 sq ft

Width: 65'

Depth: 90'

Exterior Walls: 2x6/8" cbs

Foundation: Slab

Price Code: **C4**

White Marsh Valley
Old Mill Circle

This stunning two-story home features stone and stucco to give it a wonderful street presence. Double doors open to a spacious layout that has a great room plan for comfortable living.

A warming fireplace with an entertainment center and built-ins on each side highlight the great room. This family home is a perfect example of a traditional design for today's lifestyle.

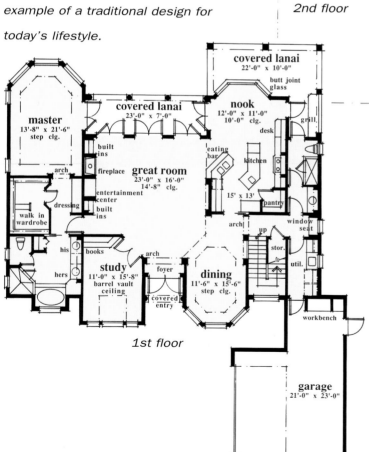

2nd floor

- observation deck
- **guest** 12'-6" x 12'-6" 9'-4" clg.
- built ins/ opt.desk
- window seat
- down
- computer desk
- **br. 2** 11'-4" x 20'-0" 9'-4" clg.

1st floor

- **covered lanai** 22'-0" x 10'-0"
- butt joint glass
- **master** 13'-8" x 21'-6" step clg.
- arch
- **covered lanai** 23'-0" x 7'-0"
- **nook** 12'-0" x 11'-0" 10'-0" clg.
- grill.
- desk
- built ins
- fireplace
- **great room** 23'-0" x 16'-0" 14'-8" clg.
- entertainment center
- built ins
- eating bar
- **kitchen**
- 15' x 13'
- pantry
- dressing
- walk in wardrobe
- his
- books
- arch
- arch
- up
- window seat
- stor.
- hers
- **study** 11'-0" x 15'-8" barrel vault ceiling
- foyer
- **dining** 11'-6" x 15'-6" step clg.
- util.
- covered entry
- workbench
- **garage** 21'-0" x 23'-0"

© The Sater Group, Inc.

© The Sater Group   6723 White Marsh Valley

© The Sater Group   6724 Old Mill Circle

Plan 6723/6724

Bedrooms: 3	Width: 65'
Baths: 3	Depth: 79'
1st Floor: 2,181 sq ft	Exterior Walls: 2X6
2nd Floor: 710 sq ft	Foundation: Slab
Living Area: 2,891 sq ft	Price Code: **C3**

blueprints
WHAT'S IN A SET?

Each set of plans is a collection of drawings — including components such as floor plans, dimensions, cross sections and elevations — that show you exactly how your house is to be built. Most of our plan packages include:

A-1 COVER SHEET/ INDEX & SITE PLAN

An Artist's Rendering of the exterior of the house shows you approximately how the house will look when built and landscaped. The Index is a list of the sheets included and page numbers for easy reference. The Site Plan is a scaled drawing of the house to help determine the placement of the home on a building site.

A-2 WALL SECTION/NOTES

This sheet shows details of the house from the roof to the foundation. This section specifies the home's construction, insulation, flooring and roofing details.

A-3 FOUNDATION PLAN

This sheet gives the foundation layout, including support walls, excavated and unexcavated areas if any, and foundation notes. If the foundation is monolithic slab rather than basement, the plan shows footing and details.

Classic Farmhouse Model 7001

DRAWING INDEX

A-1 · Site Plan, General Notes, Drawing Index
A-2 · Typical Wall Sections
A-3 · Foundation Plan and Notes
A-4 · Floor Plan and Schedules
A-5 · Ceiling Plan and Details
A-6 · Roof Plan and Notes
A-7 · Front, Rear and Left Exterior Elevations
A-8 · Right Exterior Elevation and Building Section
A-9 · Interior Elevations and Details
E-1 · Electrical Plan, Notes and Legend

Site Plan

A-1

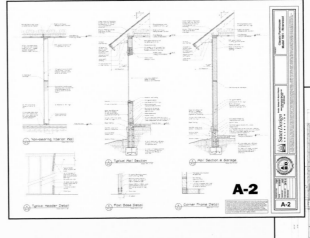

A-2

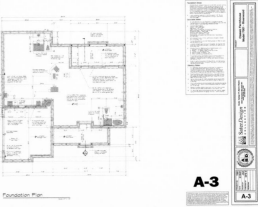

A-3

A-4 DETAILED FLOOR PLANS

These plans show the layout of each floor of the house. Rooms and interior spaces are carefully dimensioned and keys are given for cross-section details provided later in the plans, as well as window and door size callouts. These plans also show the location of kitchen appliances and bathroom fixtures.

A-5 CEILING PLAN

Sater ceiling treatments are typically very detailed. This plan shows ceiling layout and extensive detail.

A-6 ROOF PLAN

Overall layout and necessary details for roof construction are provided. If trusses are used, we suggest using a local truss manufacturer to design your trusses to comply with your local codes and regulations.

A-7 EXTERIOR ELEVATIONS

Included are front, rear, left and right sides of the house. Exterior materials, details and measurements are also given.

A-8 CROSS SECTION AND DETAILS

Important changes in floor, ceiling and roof heights or the relationship of one level to another are called out. Also shown, when applicable, are exterior details such as railing and banding.

A-9 INTERIOR ELEVATIONS

These plans show the specific details and design of cabinets, utility rooms, fireplaces, bookcases, built-in units and other special interior features depending on the nature and complexity of the item.

E-1 ELECTRICAL PLAN

This sheet shows wiring and the suggested locations for switches, fixtures and outlets.

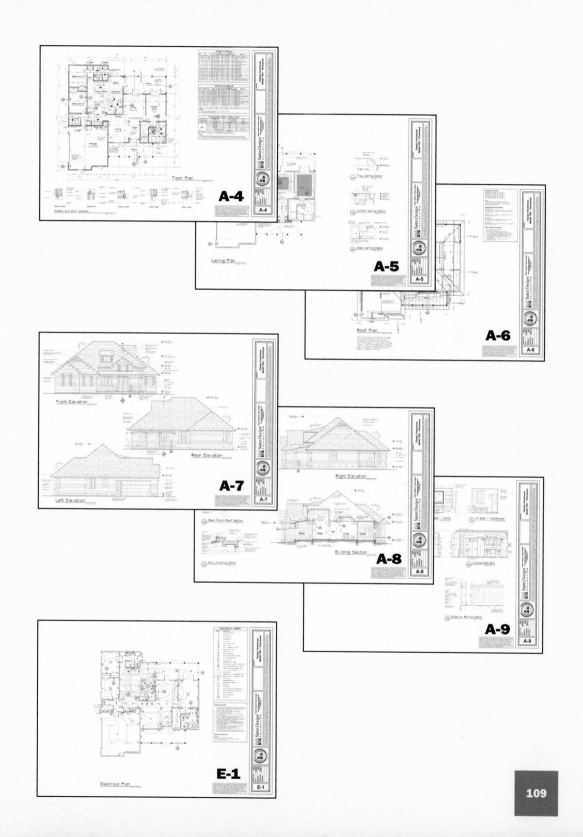

before you order

please read the following helpful information

QUICK TURNAROUND
Because you are placing your order directly, we can ship plans to you quickly. If your order is placed before noon EST, we can usually have your plans to you the next business day. Some restrictions may apply. We cannot ship to a post office box; please provide a physical street address.

OUR EXCHANGE POLICY
Since our blueprints are printed especially for you at the time you place your order, we cannot accept any returns. If, for some reason, you find that the plan that you purchased does not meet your needs, then you may exchange that plan for another plan in our collection. We allow you sixty days from the time of purchase to make an exchange. At the time of the exchange, you will be charged a processing fee of 20% of the total amount of the original order plus the difference in price between the plans (if applicable) and the cost to ship the new plans to you. Vellums cannot be exchanged. All sets must be approved and authorization given before the exchange can take place. Please call our customer service department if you have any questions.

LOCAL BUILDING CODES AND ZONING REQUIREMENTS
Our plans are designed to meet or exceed national building standards. Because of the great differences in geography and climate, each state, county and municipality has its own building codes and zoning require-ments. Your plan may need to be modified to comply with local requirements regarding snow loads, energy codes, soil and seismic condi-tions and a wide range of other matters. Prior to using plans ordered from us, we strongly advise that you consult a local building official.

ARCHITECTURE AND ENGINEERING SEALS
Some cities and states are now requiring that a licensed architect or engineer review and approve any set of building documents prior to construction. This is due to concerns over energy costs, safety, structural integrity and other factors. Prior to applying for a building permit or the start of actual construction, we strongly advise that you consult your local building official who can tell you if such a review is required.

DISCLAIMER
We have put substantial care and effort into the creation of our blueprints. We authorize the use of our blueprints on the express condition that you strictly comply with all local building codes, zoning requirements and other applicable laws, regulations and ordinances. However, because we cannot provide on-site consultation, supervision or control over actual construction, and because of the great variance in local building requirements, building practices and soil, seismic, weather and other conditions, WE CANNOT MAKE ANY WARRANTY, EXPRESS OR IMPLIED, WITH RESPECT TO THE CONTENT OR USE OF OUR BLUEPRINTS OR VELLUMS, INCLUDING BUT NOT LIMITED TO ANY WARRANTY OF MERCHANTABILITY OR OF FITNESS FOR A PARTICULAR PURPOSE.

HOW MANY SETS OF PRINTS WILL YOU NEED?
We offer a single set of prints so that you can study and plan your dream home in detail. However, you cannot build from this package. One set of blueprints is marked "NOT FOR CONSTRUCTION". If you are planning to get estimates from a contractor or subcontractor, or if you are planning to build immediately, you will need more sets. Because additional sets are less expensive, make sure you order enough to satisfy all your require-ments. Sometimes changes are needed to a plan; in that case we offer vellums that are reproducible and erasable so changes can be made directly to the plans. Vellums are the only set that can be reproduced; it is illegal to copy blueprints. The following checklist will help determine how many sets you will need:

---

plan checklist

_____ **Owner** *(one for notes, one for file set)*

_____ **Builder** *(generally requires at least three sets; one as a legal document, one for inspections and at least one to give subcontractors)*

_____ **Local Building Department** *(often requires two sets)*

_____ **Mortgage Lender** *(usually one set for a conventional loan; three sets for FHA or VA loans)*

_____ **Total Number of Sets**

IGNORING COPYRIGHT LAWS CAN BE A
$1,000,000 mistake!

Recent changes in the US copyright laws allow for statutory penalties of up to $100,000 per incident for copyright infringement involving any of the copyrighted plans found in this publication. The law can be confusing. So, for your own protection, take the time to understand what you can and cannot do when it comes to home plans.

WHAT YOU CAN'T DO!
You Cannot Duplicate Home Plans
You Cannot Copy Any Part of a Home Plan to Create Another
You Cannot Build a Home Without Buying a Blueprint or License

how to order plans

BY PHONE, BY MAIL OR ON-LINE

CALL 1-888-FLOORPLAN [356-6775]

MAIL TO: SATER DESIGN COLLECTION
25241 Elementary Way, Suite 201
Bonita Springs, Florida 34135

ADDITIONAL ITEMS

11 x 17 Color Rendering Front Perspective . .	$100.00
Additional Blueprints (per set)	$ 65.00
Reverse Blueprints (per set)	$ 50.00
Pool Plans	$225.00
Landscape Plans	$200.00
Pool & Landscape Plans	$375.00

Call for plan availability. You may special order pool or landscape packages, additional fees may apply.

POSTAGE AND HANDLING

	1-4 SETS	5 or more SETS
Overnight	$30.00	$40.00
2nd Day	$25.00	$30.00
Ground	$15.00	$18.00

International deliveries: *Please call for a quote*

Check out our extensive web sites
www.saterdesign.com
www.luxuryplans.com

BLUEPRINT PRICE SCHEDULE*

	5 SET	8 SET	VELLUM		VELLUM ONLY AVAILABLE
C1	$655	$700	$915	**PS1**	$2895
C2	$700	$745	$980	**PS2**	$3000
C3	$745	$790	$1050	**PS4**	$3585
C4	$795	$840	$1125	**PS8**	$4505
L1	$875	$925	$1240	**PSE2**	$4910
L2	$950	$1000	$1350	**PSE3**	$5135
L3	$1095	$1100	$1500	**PSE5**	$5565
L4	$1150	$1200	$1650	**PSE6**	$5770
				PSE8	$6315

* prices subject to change without notice

order form

Plan Number _____

☐ 5-set building package . . . . $_____

☐ 8-set building package . . . . $_____

☐ 1-set of reproducible vellums . . . . $_____

____ Additional Identical Blueprints @ $65 each $_____

____ Reverse Mirror-Image Blueprints @ $50 each $_____

Sub-Total $_____

Shipping and Handling $_____

Total $_____

Check one: ☐ Visa   ☐ MasterCard   ☐ AmEx

Credit Card Number _____

Name _____

Company _____

Street _____

City _____ State_____ Zip_____

Daytime Telephone Number (____)_____

Expiration Date _____

Signature _____

Check one:

☐ Consumer

☐ Builder

☐ Developer

plan index